Table of Contents

Expedition 11
Things in Motion 179

W9-CAA-861

Expedition 12
Lens on the World 199

Expedition 13
Literature and Life 219

LITERATURE CREDITS

From *Gig* edited by John Bowe, Marisa Bowe, and Sabin Streeter, copyright © 2000, 2001 by John Bowe, Marisa Bowe, and Sabin Streeter. Used by permission of Crown Publishers, a division of Random House, Inc.

From *Begging for Change*, by Sharon G. Flake, Chapter 27, pages 143–148. Jump at the Sun Hyperion Books for Children, New York. Copyright © 2003 by Sharon G. Flake.

Excerpt from *Barrio Boy* by Ernesto Galarza, pages 207–211. University of Notre Dame Press. Copyright © 1971 by University of Notre Dame Press, Notre Dame, Indiana.

Excerpt from *Dunk* by David Lubar. Text copyright © 2002 by David Lubar. Reprinted by permission of Clarion Books, an imprint of Houghton Mifflin Company. All rights reserved.

"The Stolen Bicycle" by William Saroyan as appeared in Growing Up Stories by Betsy Byars. Reprinted by permission of the Trustees of Leland Stanford Junior University.

"No League of Their Own; Barred from all-white leagues, three women found a place to play" by Dan Silverman, from Major League Baseball website, www.mlb.com. Reprinted with permission of Dan Silverman.

From The *Autobiography of Malcolm X*, by Malcolm X with Alex Haley. Ballantine Books, a division of Random House, Inc., New York. Copyright © 1965 by Alex Haley and Betty Shabazz.

Excerpt from Juan Williams' radio interview with Muhammad Ali. NPR Web site at www.npr.org.

PHOTO AND ART CREDITS

Cover: Goodshoot/SuperStock

Title page: Goodshoot/SuperStock

Expedition 11: 179, SuperStock; p180-181, 183-186, AP; 189-190, iStock; 191, Corbis; 195, 196-198, AP

Expedition 12: 199, 200, 201, SuperStock; 203-206, Russell Moore; 207-211, 215-217, iStock

Expedition 13: 219, SuperStock; 220, Corbis; 224, AP; 225, 229, AP; 230, David Griffin; 233, AP; 234, Russell Moore; 238, AP; 239-242, David Griffin

Expedition 14: 243, SuperStock; 244, Corbis; 247, 249, AP; 250, 253, iStock; 256, 157, 258, 260-261, AP; 267, iStock

Expedition 15: 271, SuperStock; 272, Corbis; 276, 279, iStock; 280, AP; 285, iStock; 289, AP; 291, iStock

ISBN 1-4168-0845-0

Copyright 2006 by Voyager Expanded Learning, L.P.

Printed in the United States of America   05 06 07 08 09 10 11 DIG 9 8 7 6 5 4 3 2 1

THINGS IN MOTION

- *In what ways do people use motion for fun?*

- *What things affect how fast an object can go?*

- *How can understanding motion help athletes achieve success?*

Pocket Bikes

VS.

Motorcycles

[1]Some people think pocket bikes are the hottest things on wheels. Others call them death on wheels. One thing is certain, though. These child-sized motorcycles have revved up a lot of debate. Pocket bikes are similar to motorcycles in many ways. Like motorcycles, pocket bikes have two wheels. The rider sits on a seat and steers with handlebars. But pocket bikes and motorcycles are different in one important way—size. Pocket bikes are about half as big as motorcycles. That appeals to pocket bike fans. "They're so cute," says one owner. "That's the main thing." Not everyone agrees. Some people say safety is the main thing. Pocket bikes might be cuter than motorcycles. But they also can be much more dangerous.

What Are They?

[2]Pocket bikes are designed to resemble motorcycles. Some look like choppers. They have long forks on the front wheel. Others look more like racing motorcycles. They are painted with colorful numbers and designs. Still others look like off-road motorcycles. They have knobby tires to grip muddy roads. But park a pocket bike next to a motorcycle and you will easily see the difference. Pocket bikes are much smaller. Motorcycles are about as big as an adult's 10-speed bicycle. Pocket bikes, on the other hand, are about the size of a child's tricycle. Pocket bikes are so tiny that adults have to squat to sit on the seats. Their knees stick up in the air. By contrast, adults can sit on motorcycles just like they sit in chairs.

[3]Another thing that is smaller about pocket bikes is their price. Pocket bikes cost much less money than motorcycles. The cheapest pocket bikes are **manufactured** in China. Some cost less than $200. Pocket bikes for racing are usually made in Italy. They can cost a few thousand dollars. Motorcycles also come in a range of prices. The cheapest ones cost about $6,000. Some cost as much as fancy cars.

[4]Both pocket bikes and motorcycles are powered by engines. The engines might run on gas, or they might be electric. That's where the similarities end. Pocket bikes have much smaller engines. Their engines are about the size of some lawn mower engines. Even with these small engines, pocket bikes can really move. They can travel at speeds **approaching** 30 miles per hour. Motorcycles, on the other hand, have much larger engines. A motorcycle engine can be 20 times more powerful than a pocket bike engine. Motorcycles can go much faster than pocket bikes. Most motorcycles can go more than 100 miles per hour.

Who Rides Them?

[5]Pocket bikes are a **global** hit. Stores all over the world sell them. Hundreds of thousands of people have bought pocket bikes. Dave Green, who sells pocket bikes near Boston, says he has grown **accustomed** to adults buying them. "They say they're buying them for their children,

but then I see them out riding them," he says. Still, a lot of pocket bike riders are children. On the other hand, children almost never ride motorcycles. That's because states treat motorcycles the same as cars. To ride a motorcycle, you have to be old enough for a driver's license. By contrast, few states require pocket bike riders to have a license. That makes it easier for children to ride them.

Are They Safe?

[6]Many people think pocket bikes are much more dangerous than motorcycles. Pocket bikes cause a lot of tension among police, who worry that riders might get hurt. "They're pretty much death on wheels," says Deputy Pete Maurer of Florida. A magazine that rates product safety calls pocket bikes "a bad bet." The magazine asked scientists to test a lot of pocket bikes. Many had poor brakes, which can make stopping harder. That can cause accidents bad enough to break bones. Some people have even been killed in pocket bike wrecks. Another important difference between motorcycles and pocket bikes is safety **features**. Things such as turn signals and mirrors can help prevent accidents. Motorcycles are required by law to have these safety items. Many pocket bikes, however, have no safety items at all. Size is another problem. Unlike motorcycles, pocket bikes are so small that it is hard for car drivers to see them.

[7]Some people say pocket bikes can be as safe as motorcycles if they are used correctly. Still, experts warn pocket bikers to stay off city streets. Pocket bikes should be ridden only in backyards or on approved tracks. Experts also tell pocket bike riders to use special gear that provides protection in case of accidents. For example, a leather body suit should always be worn. "Without a suit, you're going to lose skin," says Frank Smith, a 34-year-old pocket bike racer. To be safe, pocket bikers should also wear gloves, helmets, and pads on their elbows and knees, experts say.

[8]Pocket bikes and motorcycles might look alike, but they have very different uses. Motorcycles are for riding on public roads. Not only are they bigger and easier to see, but they also have better safety items. Pocket bikes, on the other hand, can be a lot of fun if used safely. That means riders should keep them off public streets and wear safety gear. As 17-year-old pocket biker Robert Moir of Florida says, "They're only dangerous if you get stupid with them."

Lance Armstrong's bicycle is designed to give him an edge when racing.

AGAINST THE WIND

[1]To most people, a breeze is just a cool break on a warm day. For a bicycle racer like Lance Armstrong, however, a little breeze can be a big problem. If you have ever peddled a bike into a stiff wind, you know why. The wind pushes back on you as you peddle forward. This is called wind drag. It slows you down. It makes you peddle harder. It might even make you a little late to your friend's house. No big deal, right? It is to Lance. Wind drag can turn a win into a loss. To make sure that doesn't happen, Lance hired a team of experts to come up with solutions to the problem of wind drag. As a result of their work, Lance reduced wind drag to a **minimum**. That helped him become one of the greatest bike racers ever.

183

Every Second Counts

[2]Lance is very competitive. He wants to win every race. But his main goal every year is to win the Tour de France. This **international** bicycle race draws the best riders from all over the world. The riders race almost every day for 3 weeks. They ride for more than 2,100 miles before the race is over. That's like riding a bike from Los Angeles to Atlanta. It's a long race, but the margin of victory can be just a few seconds. In 1989, the first and second place riders were separated by only 8 seconds. In 2003, Lance won the race by 61 seconds.

[3]Since every second counts, Lance's experts work year round to give him the winning edge. One goal is to reduce the weight of his bicycle frame. The frame is what the wheels, seat, and handlebars are attached to. Lance's experts made a new bike frame. They used super-light material—the kind that is used in airplanes. As a result, Lance's bike frame weighs less than 3 pounds. That's almost as light as a paperback book. It is also as light as racing rules allow.

[4]Since they could not make the bike lighter, Lance's team worked on reducing the wind drag. Less wind drag means that Lance can ride faster while using less energy. Even a slight decrease in energy used makes a difference. Saving just 10 watts of energy can cut Lance's time in a 120-mile race by 1 minute. It doesn't take much to save 10 watts of energy. Cleaning a dirty bike chain will do it. Lance's experts looked at every possible way to reduce wind drag. They rebuilt his bike. They adjusted his riding position. They even changed his clothes to reduce wind drag. No change was too small.

The Bike Frame

[5]Lance's experts used a wind tunnel to test different bike frames. A wind tunnel is a giant machine that blows wind past an object. It allows scientists to measure the **effect** of the wind on the object. Bike frames made of round tubes did poorly in the wind tunnel. The wind caused too much drag. So Lance's experts

decided to come up with a new shape. They used a computer to test ideas. Once they decided on a shape, they had a team of bike builders put together a new frame by hand. After the frame was **assembled**, Lance's experts tested it in a wind tunnel. The results were impressive. The new frame reduced wind drag, so Lance was able to ride faster.

The Wheels

[6]Most bicycles have wheels with metal spokes. These wheels work great on regular bikes. They cause problems on racing bikes, though. The spokes stir up air like an egg beater stirs up eggs. To solve this problem, new wheel designs were tested in wind tunnels. Lance's experts decided on a wheel with just three spokes. These spokes are shaped like airplane wings, so they cut through the wind. As a result, the new wheels caused less wind drag.

The Seat Post

[7]Another problem faced by Lance's experts was caused by the post that holds the bike seat. Lance leans forward on his handlebars when he races. This funnels wind down his chest, under the seat, and past the seat post. A poorly designed seat post can cause a lot of wind drag. That can cost Lance a race. To solve this problem, Lance's experts tested different seat posts in the wind tunnel. They found that round seat posts increase wind drag. The solution was to design a new and **unique** way to hold the seat on the bike. Lance's team replaced the post with a tube shaped like an airplane wing. This tube holds the seat in place. It also reduces wind drag.

The Clothes

[8]About two-thirds of the wind drag Lance feels comes from his body. The problem is that the human body is not designed to cut through the wind. Lance's experts came up with three solutions.

- Body Position: Lance practiced riding his bike in a wind tunnel. He tried different positions to see which one reduced wind drag the most. Even a minor change, like sticking out a thumb, can create enough wind drag to cause a rider to lose a race. As a result of his experiments, Lance found the perfect body position for reducing wind drag.
- Clothes: Lance worked with a sports company to design a new riding suit. The company tried dozens of different suits and fabrics. The result was a suit made of several fabrics with different textures. Most of Lance's suit is made of very smooth material. Some parts are made with fabric that has tiny dimples. These little dents in the fabric help direct wind around Lance's body. That helps reduce wind drag even more. Wind tunnel tests showed that the suit could cut 90 seconds off Lance's time in a 34-mile race.
- Helmet: Lance's team also designed a new helmet. Like everything else, Lance's new helmet was tested in a wind tunnel. The helmet's design reduced wind drag. Consequently, Lance was able to go faster in the wind tunnel.

The Difference

[9]Lance Armstrong is a gifted athlete. He works hard every day to improve. But other bike racers also are gifted and hardworking. Lance depends on his team of experts to keep him ahead of the other racers. The experts helped Lance win the Tour de France seven straight times. People once thought such a record was **impossible**. But Lance proved it could be done, with a little help from his team of experts.

Skateboarders deserve a place to practice.

¹To the Editor of *The Greendale Times:*

²If you play a team sport in this city, you have it made. Greendale City Park has five soccer fields and nine baseball fields. Every school in town has a football field and an indoor basketball court. There are plenty of opportunities for teens who want to play a team sport. But what if your sport is skateboarding? Then you are out of luck. Skateboarding is off limits in all **public** areas of Greendale. You can't skateboard on parking lots or sidewalks. Skateboarding is not allowed on neighborhood streets or in parks. These places are supposed to belong to all of us. Yet those of us who ride skateboards are not allowed to use them. Football players aren't allowed to play in the streets, either, but they have other places to play. Skateboarders

187

do not. That's wrong, and the best way to make it right is to build a skatepark.

[3]Skateboarding was not always against the law here. A few years ago, we could ride our skateboards anywhere we wanted. Then the "No Skateboard" signs started appearing. As soon we found a good place to skateboard, one of those signs would go up. So we would relocate to another place. Then another sign would pop up. Before long, there was almost no place in the city to skateboard. Then the city council voted to ban skateboarding almost everywhere. The only place we can skateboard now is on our driveways.

[4]Why do people single out skateboards? Some say skateboards should be banned because they damage property. True, skateboards sometimes scratch sidewalks and curbs. But it's not like curbs and sidewalks are **ancient** treasures that must be protected. Also, BMX bikes cause damage, and nobody wants to ban them. Others say it's because skateboarders frighten people who are walking on the sidewalks. If you use that **logic**, you would also have to ban inline skates. But have you ever seen a sign that says "No Skating"? I haven't either. Still others insist that skateboarders are rude. It's true that we sometimes skate pretty fast. But we're not doing it to be rude. Skateboards do not have speedometers, so we don't always know how fast we're going. Besides, how many times have you seen someone act rude while driving a car? Should we also ban cars because of a few rude drivers?

Skateboarding Versus Team Sports

[5]Few people argue when the city spends money on team sports. That's because playing a physical game like basketball is a great way for kids to stay in shape. But not all teens are into team sports. Those games seem to be mainly about learning complicated rules and dividing people into teams of winners and losers. As one great football coach said, "Winning isn't everything … it's the *only* thing." That attitude is why some don't like team sports. When winning is "the only thing," teens who are less talented rarely get to play. They wind up sitting on the bench watching other kids play. How is that any better than sitting on a couch watching TV?

[6]In skateboarding, you never have to worry about the rejection of sitting on the bench. Everybody plays. There are no rules. Nobody keeps score. That's because skateboarding isn't about winning and losing. It's about working hard and trying your best. But mostly it's about expressing yourself and getting a little exercise. That way kids who aren't into team sports can have fun and improve their physical fitness.

The Skatepark Solution

[7]If city leaders are going to ban skateboards from the sidewalks, then the least they can do is give us a place to play. Skateboarders are citizens too. We deserve a park as much as the kids who play baseball do. Yes, a skatepark would cost money. So do baseball fields, and they are not used most of the year. Even during baseball season, only a few players at a time can play on a field. By contrast, even a small skatepark can hold 100 skateboarders at a time. And skateparks stay open year round. What's more, the city could help pay for the skatepark by charging admission and selling food and drinks.

[8]A skatepark would have many benefits. For example, cities that have built skateparks have noticed that teens commit fewer crimes. In Edinburgh, Scotland, teens spent 4 years trying to talk city leaders into building a skatepark. When the park opened in 2003, police noticed a big drop in crime among teens. When Windham, Maine, opened a skatepark, arrests fell by 40 percent. Drug arrests fell even more, by 75 percent. A report by the Windham police department said that the skateboarders were keeping the park clean and behaving respectfully to the people who work at the park. That sounds like exactly the way adults are always telling us teens to behave.

[9]Reducing crime isn't the only advantage. A skatepark will also make kids smarter. In 1998, a skateboarding magazine asked its readers about their grades. A third of skateboarders were A students and half were B students. Only 1 percent of skateboarders were failing in school. Obviously, skateboarding is not keeping kids away from their schoolwork.

189

A Safe Way to Play

[10]Many people **consider** skateboarding a dangerous sport. They think skateboarders are always busting their skulls or breaking their legs. Sure, skateboarders sometimes get hurt. But there is plenty of **evidence** that skateboarding is safer than most sports, and I'm not just talking about football. According to a federal government study, teens are twice as likely to get hurt playing basketball or baseball as they are by skateboarding. Many parents want their kids to play soccer because they think it's safe. But the government study says that skateboarding is even safer than soccer.

[11]A skatepark can reduce the risk of injuries even more. A 2002 study found that one out of every three accidents happened the first week after receiving a skateboard. A skatepark could offer safety classes for beginners. That way, fewer would get hurt. A skatepark could also require wearing safety gear. Right now, most skateboarders in town don't wear helmets, elbow and knee pads, or wrist guards. If more skateboarders wear this kind of gear, there will be even fewer injuries.

A Cool Place for a Cool Sport

[12]Skateboarding is the coolest sport in the world. It gets more popular every year. Good skateboarders can even become professionals, just like football, basketball, or baseball players. But to make it to the pros, skateboarders need places to practice. It would be great if there were dozens of places around town where kids could skateboard without bothering people. But those places do not **exist**. That's why the city should build a skatepark.

Mike Marshall set pitching records that have lasted 30 years.

A Pitching Machine

[1]When he was 11 years old, Mike Marshall was in a car wreck. It changed his life, but not in the way you might expect—and not for another 10 years. Marshall's back hurt for years after the accident. It still hurt when he started playing professional baseball after high school. Marshall planned to play pro baseball in the minor leagues for a couple of years. Then, if he was good enough, he hoped to play in the major leagues.

[2]At first Marshall played shortstop. As a shortstop, he had to bend over every time he caught a ground ball. Bending over was hard, because his back was not as flexible as it had been before the car wreck. The back pain also kept Marshall from practicing to become a better shortstop, so he made a lot of mistakes during games.

[3]It was beginning to look as if Marshall would never **recover** from his back injury. Without a healthy back, he had no chance of playing shortstop in the major leagues. Then Marshall had an idea. His bad back would be less of a problem if he were a pitcher. Pitchers don't have to bend over as often as shortstops do. So in 1964, he told his coaches that he wanted to become a pitcher. Finally, he had found a way to get to the major leagues.

Learning to Pitch

[4]There was one thing about pitching that worried Marshall. Pitchers often hurt their arms. Sometimes the injuries are so bad that the players can never pitch again. Marshall had already given up on playing shortstop because of an injury. He didn't want his pitching career to end the same way.

[5]To avoid that fate, Marshall had to use his **intelligence** as much as his body. First, he borrowed a special slow-motion camera. Next, he filmed himself throwing a baseball. After that, he used the film to study his pitching motion. Marshall also went to college to learn more about how the human body moved. Marshall used this knowledge to deconstruct the traditional pitching motion. By taking it apart, Marshall could look closely at every little part of the pitching motion. His studies convinced him that the traditional motion had a lot of wasted movements that were actually hurting pitchers. Marshall developed a pitching motion that was completely different from the traditional motion. With his **unusual** new motion, Marshall could throw the ball faster and more often without getting a sore arm.

[6]Marshall's coaches had **doubts** about his ability to pitch with this new motion. They told him to use the regular pitching motion. Marshall refused. "I figured it's my life, my career," he said. "I'm in charge of it." As a result,

1954	1964	1967	1970	1973
Mike Marshall injures his back in a car accident.	Marshall decides to become a baseball pitcher.	Marshall is promoted to the major leagues.	Marshall is traded to a team that lets him pitch the way he wants.	Marshall pitches in 92 of his team's 162 games.

192

Marshall's team traded him to another team. His new coaches liked what they saw, and in 1967 Marshall was promoted to the major leagues. Marshall pitched very well, but he continued to disobey his coaches. He would not pitch the way they wanted. He would not practice the way they wanted. He was certain his way of pitching was better. Finally, the coaches decided to send Marshall back to the minor leagues.

[7]By 1969, Marshall was back in the major leagues with a different team. He still argued with his coaches about the best way to pitch. At the end of the season, he was traded again. Then, shortly after the 1970 season started, Marshall was traded yet again. This time, however, Marshall found a coach who agreed with him. For the first time in his career, Marshall would not have to **convince** his coach to let him pitch the way he wanted.

[8]In baseball, the pitcher who throws the first pitch of the game is called the starting pitcher. When he gets tired or when the other team scores too many runs, he is replaced by a relief pitcher. By 1973, Marshall was one of the best relief pitchers in baseball. He set a record by pitching in 92 out of his team's 162 games. The Los Angeles Dodgers decided that they needed a pitcher like Marshall, so they traded for him.

A Record-Setting Season

[9]At the start of the 1974 season, Marshall's new manager asked him how often he wanted to pitch. "I'll let you know if I'm not able to pitch on a certain day," Marshall told him. "Otherwise you can pitch me every day if you feel I can help you win a ball game." The coach said, "Sounds good to me."

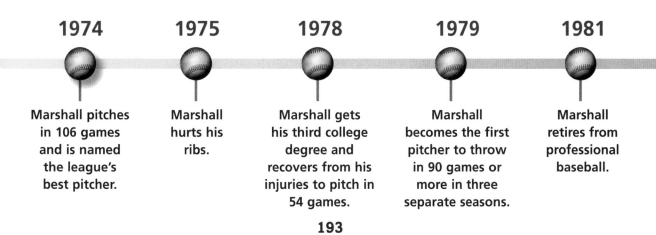

1974	**1975**	**1978**	**1979**	**1981**
Marshall pitches in 106 games and is named the league's best pitcher.	Marshall hurts his ribs.	Marshall gets his third college degree and recovers from his injuries to pitch in 54 games.	Marshall becomes the first pitcher to throw in 90 games or more in three separate seasons.	Marshall retires from professional baseball.

[10]Soon Marshall was pitching almost every game. On July 3, he set a major league record by pitching in his thirteenth straight game. The next day, he pitched again. Through it all, Marshall's arm never hurt. His back was another story. "At times with the Dodgers I would have to crawl into the trainer's room," Marshall says. "He would twist me and turn me to get my back in shape to pitch that day." With the help of the trainer, Marshall kept pitching and pitching. By the end of the season, he had pitched in 106 games. It was a new record, and it has never been broken. After the 1974 season, Marshall became the first relief pitcher to be named the best pitcher in the league.

[11]The next few seasons were difficult for Marshall. In 1975, he hurt his ribs and missed a lot of games. Then he missed a lot more games to have surgery on his back. The operation left his back pain-free for the first time since the car accident. But then he hurt his knee. He wasn't fully healthy until 1978, when he pitched in 54 games. That same year, Marshall earned his third degree from Michigan State University. The next season, Marshall pitched in 90 games. He is still the only pitcher to throw in 90 or more games in three different seasons. Despite all that pitching, Marshall never hurt his arm. "People said, 'This is a physical freak,' and I'm not," Marshall says. "I trained my arm to do it day after day after day, and I did it."

Retired, But Still Working

[12]Marshall retired from professional baseball in 1981. But he didn't stop pitching. Instead, he moved to Florida and pitched in amateur leagues. "I just love pitching," Marshall says. "I was undefeated for over 10 years." Marshall

pitched in at least 80 games a season for the next three decades.

[13]Today, Marshall teaches his **methods** to young players. "The kids who come to me don't get college scholarships or they can't make the team or they've had injuries," Marshall says. After learning how to pitch Marshall's way, many of the young players wind up getting college scholarships. But most important, Marshall says, "No pitcher I've trained has had a pitching arm injury."

Faster than Sound

In 1947, Chuck Yeager became the first person to go faster than the speed of sound in an airplane.

Fifty years later, Andy Green became the first to break the sound barrier in a car.

[1]Ever since cars and airplanes were invented, people have wanted to go faster and faster. At first, they were happy to race each other. But as airplanes and cars improved, people turned their attention to other challenges. Racing other airplanes and cars was fine. But the real challenge was racing sound. Simply put, they wanted to go faster than sound travels.

[2]Although they were separated by 50 years, the efforts to break the speed of sound in the air and on land were similar in many ways. Both featured a race that was the first of its kind to pass the speed of sound. In each case, the top competitors were from America and England. However, a different country won each race. In the air, America won. On the ground, England won.

What's That Noise?

[3]To understand the speed of sound, think about a fireworks display. As you watch from the ground, the fireworks shoot high into the air. You see them explode in a riot of color. Then, a split second later, you hear the explosion of the fireworks. That split second was how long it took sound to travel from the explosion high in the air to your ear closer to the ground. Sound travels at different speeds depending on several factors. For example, sound travels faster through air than through water. Sound also travels faster closer to the ground than it does high up in the sky. Temperature and humidity also play a role in the exact speed that sound travels. For example, at sea level with a temperature of 59 degrees, sound travels at about 761 miles an hour. At the altitude that many airplanes fly, sound travels about 100 miles per hour slower.

[4]When something passes the speed of sound, a very loud noise results. This noise is called a sonic boom. It's louder than the loudest firecracker you've ever heard. The noise is caused by shock waves. As an airplane flies, it pushes air molecules out of the way. That creates waves of air. These waves are like the ripples in water. When the airplane passes the speed of sound, the waves of air are pressed together into shock waves. These shock waves rocket away from the airplane toward the ground. When the shock waves hit your eardrum, you hear a sonic boom.

FIRST SUPERSONIC FLIGHT 1947

USA 32

Flying Faster Than Sound

[5]Chuck Yeager, a 24-year-old American pilot, was the first person to travel fast enough to create a sonic boom. Yeager broke the sound barrier in a top-secret military airplane called the X-1. "Basically, the X-1 was pure rocket," Yeager says. This "bullet with wings" was about 31 feet long and weighed 12,250 pounds. It was powered by a rocket engine with four chambers. Each chamber could be fired separately to make the plane faster.

[6]On October 14, 1947, Yeager climbed aboard a large cargo airplane. The rocket plane was strapped to the belly of the cargo plane. The cargo plane flew to a height of 25,000 feet. Yeager climbed down a ladder to the rocket

This jet-powered car reached a speed of 448 miles per hour during a trial run in 1996.

plane and crawled into the cockpit. The rocket plane was released. As it fell through the air, the rocket plane went faster and faster. Then Yeager switched on the first chamber of the rocket engine. The plane burst forward. Then Yeager switched on the other three chambers, one at a time. As each chamber fired, the rocket plane flew a little faster. When the plane approached the speed of sound, it began to shake and bounce harder and harder. Then the plane passed the sound barrier. All the shaking and rattling stopped. Yeager had done it! He had become the first person to travel faster than sound.

Driving Faster Than Sound

[7]On October 13, 1997, a 35-year-old British pilot named Andy Green climbed into a jet-powered car. It was parked on the hard ground in the Nevada desert. The car was about 54 feet long and weighed about 20,000 pounds. Two jet engines were attached to the car, one on each side. The engines had been removed from jet planes. Green made three runs on a 13-mile course that day. On the first run, the car reached a top speed that was just a little slower than sound. On the second run, Green pushed the jet car just a little faster. A sonic boom rattled the desert. Then something scary happened. The parachute that was to help stop the car did not open. Green managed to stop the jet car. But he had overshot the end of the course by a mile and a half. It took 61 minutes to turn the car around and get it ready for

another run. Green also broke the speed of sound on the third run. But too much time had passed between the two runs. A driver must make two runs within 60 minutes to set a world record. So Green and his crew tried again two days later. This time they topped the speed of sound twice in less than an hour. They made the record official on the day after the fiftieth anniversary of Yeager's flight.

The Competition

[8]Yeager and Green weren't the only ones trying to break the speed of sound. Yeager faced competition from an airplane designed and flown in England. That plane crashed about a year before Yeager's successful flight, killing the pilot. By contrast, Green's main competition came from America. The driver of that car crashed almost a year before Green broke the sound barrier. Unlike Yeager's competitor, however, the driver of the car from America walked away from the crash.

[9]The world did not find out about Yeager's flight for 7 months. That's because the rocket plane was a military secret. By contrast, news of Green's ride was in newspapers all over the world the next day. Today, both Yeager's rocket airplane and Green's jet car are in museums. By traveling faster than sound, Yeager and Green eliminated a major barrier to how fast humans can go.

Crew members work on this 47-foot long rocket car powered by a modified F-4 Phantom jet engine.

LENS ON THE WORLD

- *What creates your lens on the world?*
- *Why do people see the same thing differently?*
- *What makes a place feel like "home"?*

Two Views

Dear Aunt Julia,

[1]Our new life began 2 months ago, but I still feel like I'm in a dream. I should be used to my new **surroundings** by now, shouldn't I? Momma keeps saying, "You'll grow to like Chicago, if you give it half a chance." I tell her I might've liked Chicago better if I hadn't been shoved here by wind and water.

[2]I miss Bayview and my friends and you and Uncle Leo. I miss the salty air and the bright sun and the comforting smell of your homemade rolls. Just look what that stupid hurricane did! It shredded our house and blew us hundreds of miles from home, and it forced you and Uncle Leo to move to Texas, where you're probably dodging tumbleweeds all day. (With all those cows in Texas, better watch where you step, Auntie.) What's Texas like, anyway?

[3]Leesha and I go to a school 3 blocks from our apartment. The school is about 10 times larger than our old school, and it looks like a sad old factory. When the bell rings, hundreds of kids spill into the halls, chattering like the seagulls near the fishing pier back home. I keep to myself—you know how I am—but Leesha has already made about a thousand friends. People here are crazy about sports. Maybe if I were more athletic I'd make friends faster.

[4]Well, actually, I've made one friend. His name is Curtis, and he just moved here last year, so he knows what it's like to adjust to a new place.

[5]There's more to do here than in Bayview, especially since Bayview is probably a muddy ghost town by now. There are museums and shops and all kinds of restaurants, if you like those things. Pizza is good here. But there are too many people! You have to wait in a lot of lines. Our family rode the subway to a **recent** baseball game, and we were so mashed together on the

# of Chicago

Teenagers, even those from the same family, can have very different points of view.

cars I could hardly breathe. But the game was exciting, especially when a batter would crack the ball out of the park or when the ball would go *whap* in a player's glove.

[6]The city bumps up against Lake Michigan, and there's a busy port here. When you drive outside the city, you see cows grazing in the fields, like in Texas, maybe. I like the countryside more than the city. I'm dreading winter, because I hear that the cold bites your nose and freezes your bones.

[7]I miss you and I miss my old life, which is pretty **obvious**, isn't it? I miss the slower pace and the familiar faces. Maybe I *am* dreaming after all, and I'll wake up in my own bed back home and ride over to your house for breakfast!

Love, Deon

Dear Carol-Lee,

[8]Thanks for your birthday card. I'm glad you were able to get our new address from Mrs. Simms. We've been in Chicago for about 2 months, and I'm loving it already. Having to leave Bayview was sad, especially since the awful hurricane was headed our way and was likely to swallow up the whole town (which it did), but at least we got out safely. So did everyone else in our little community, but now we've scattered to the four winds.

[9]Speaking of winds, did you know that Chicago is known as the Windy

City? The wind blows off Lake Michigan, a lake as big as the ocean. And guess what? They actually have WINTER here! I can't wait to see snow. Momma says we'll all need heavy coats and gloves.

[10]We live just outside the city in an apartment. You would LOVE the city. It buzzes with cars and people and places to go! On weekends, the sidewalks overflow with eager tourists and bustling residents. You've never seen such an **assortment** of faces and clothing and styles!

[11]Oh—and the elevated trains! Pop took all of us to a baseball game here. I didn't care much for the game, but riding the "el" to the game and back was a real adventure—like being at a bazaar in a faraway country. At one of the stops, I smelled a strange, delicious odor, which Momma said was curry, a sauce made from **particular** spices. I saw an elegant woman with a gold scarf wrapped around her head. I listened to two people speaking a language I've never heard.

[12]Deon and I can walk to our school, which is in a beautiful old red-brick building that feels solid and dignified, like a college in the East. I've made several friends there already. Deon is taking his time making friends, as you might guess. You know how shy he is. I tease him about being an old hermit crab! He grumbles about everything here. I guess I'm just more **flexible** than Deon is when it comes to change.

[13]I miss my friends from Bayview, but I could never go back to my dull little life there, even if they rebuilt the town. There's just so much LIFE here, and it's so varied.

[14]I hope you're doing fine and that you can come visit me soon. There's so much to show you. Thanks again for the birthday card.

```
Your friend,
Leesha
```

LEAVING HOME

¹**R**osa wasn't sure she had slept at all, when she felt Pancho's paw on her arm. It was 4:00 in the morning. Just as she had many times before, Rosa climbed out of bed and slipped into her jeans and mudboots. Papí was making coffee down the hall. Rosa paused in the kitchen doorway, admiring the oak-like frame of her father and the confidence of his movements. She kissed his cheek and let Pancho out the back door.

²"You don't have to get up so early *today*," said Papí. "Tito can do your chores. You need to rest for your journey."

³"I know, Papí," Rosa said. "But I feel so strange. The **routine** will help, and I want to say good-bye to my four-legged sisters and brothers." Rosa walked out the door and bent to rub Pancho's head. A knot formed in her throat. Not

now, she told herself, willing the tears back. The air was cool. A mist hung over the horse pasture, and a faint ribbon of pink streaked across the eastern sky.

⁴Walking toward the barn, Rosa had the sensation that she was seeing everything for the first time: the leaning clothesline, the weathered barn, the comical scarecrow in the garden. Every tree, every bush, every clod of dirt seemed a part of her and she a part of it.

⁵All that she saw contained memories and associations. She recalled the day a peacock appeared from nowhere and perched atop one of the clothesline posts. After a few hours, the bird floated down as lightly as a cloud and strutted about the yard, **revealing** its showy tail feathers, until Pancho chased it into the woods.

⁶Entering the barn, she remembered an afternoon nearly a decade ago when Papí let her help one of the heifers give birth to a calf. The memory was still vivid, of Papí's showing her how to grasp the slippery front legs of the calf at just the right moment, and pull the animal out of its trembling mother. She remembered how she insisted on naming the calf Cinderella, even though it was a bull.

⁷As Rosa went about her tasks, every motion seemed charged with meaning. She patted the horses' flanks and scratched the heads of the goats. She recalled the day her pet goat, Lulu, became sick and lay near the porch until Mamí wrapped her in blankets and set her near the fireplace. "Lulu is dying," Mamí said gently. Rosa was a small girl and did not understand, but the next day, when the light went out of her pet's eyes, Rosa saw how those she loved could be taken far beyond her reach.

⁸"I can't leave"—Rosa reasoned to herself—"in spite of the scholarship, in spite of the chance to **pursue** my dream. Going away to boarding school is **illogical**, a silly plan." Then an idea occurred to her: she would pretend to be sick. The bus would have to leave without her, and she could stay in her familiar world, after all!

⁹Mamí was preparing breakfast when Rosa appeared in the kitchen. "Mamí, I think I'm sick!" Rosa said, clutching her stomach. "I can't go away

today." Rosa's mother turned from the stove and looked at her daughter with concern. For a moment, Rosa was distracted by the odor of her mother's homemade biscuits. "I'll—uh—go lie down for a minute," she said.

[10]Rosa's thoughts were a **turbulent** swirl as she lay down. Her father soon appeared in her room and asked in a booming voice, "What's this I hear?"

[11]"Oh, Papí," Rosa said, as the tears came. "I was pretending to be sick so I wouldn't have to leave!"

[12]Papí patted his daughter's hand. "I know," he said. "But you worked hard to get the scholarship, so you must give it a try. When you can't see our faces anymore, you'll feel better. Now, let's go eat those biscuits Mamí made for us."

[13]After breakfast, Rosa showered and dressed for her journey. Tito put her bags in the car. Then Rosa stood on the front porch while Mamí took her picture. After that, she said good-bye to Pancho and took a final look around—at the vegetable garden, whose weeds and bugs had given her fits last summer, and the milking shed, where she'd toiled sleepily on many a cold morning. The family got into the car, and as they rolled down the dirt driveway, Rosa watched the farm slowly disappear behind her like a ghost.

[14]Papí stopped the car at the turn-off to the main road and unloaded Rosa's suitcases. Rosa breathed in the sweet odor of honeysuckle. Mamí handed her a sack of sandwiches and cookies. Tito perked his ears and announced that the bus was approaching. He and his sister exchanged a brief glance before Tito looked away.

¹⁵The bus stopped near the family. The driver opened the door and called hello to the family. A tall woman in a brown suit emerged from the bus and introduced herself as Ms. Hill, the official greeter for the school. "You must be our scholar," she said, smiling at Rosa, who nodded shyly in **response**. "I'll accompany you to the school today," she explained.

¹⁶When it was time to say good-bye, Mamí hugged Rosa, and both of them began to cry. Papí looked into his daughter's eyes and then hugged her tightly. "Good luck," he said. "Remember how much we love you."

¹⁷Tito looked at the ground and nudged a rock with his foot before accepting a hug from his sister. "Take care of Pancho and do well in school and don't forget your chores." Tito nodded and tried to say something but his throat was too tight.

¹⁸Rosa climbed on the bus and sat near a window. She waved to her family. Mamí was still crying. Papí had one broad arm around her and was waving with the other. Tito waved and squinted in the sun. Ms. Hill sat down next to Rosa.

¹⁹Rosa didn't feel like talking to Ms. Hill or anybody for a while. The bus driver started the engine and steered onto the main road. Rosa kept looking at her family until they were a tiny speck in the distance. Then the bus went over a hill, and she couldn't see them at all anymore.

²⁰After a while, Rosa began to feel better. Perhaps Papí was right, she thought, as she watched the land become hillier and greener. She caught herself thinking, "No more getting up at four in the morning, no more milking cows in the cold shed, no more weeding the garden!"

²¹Rosa opened the sack Mamí had given her. She took out two cookies and handed one of them to Ms. Hill.

New York, New York

[1]**Saturday morning, June 12**   Finally! We're on the road. We were supposed to leave on our trip an hour ago but were **delayed** by the sudden disappearance of my brother Will's pet rat. The squeaky little fur-ball squirted out of Will's hands as he was introducing it to his friend who's supposed to watch it while we're gone.

[2]Mom found the disgusting little rodent under a cabinet. Will actually cried like a baby when he thought his beloved pet was lost. Bet he wouldn't cry if I were lost. Anyhow, this is supposed to be an account of our trip to New York City, not a news bulletin about a missing rat.

³**Sunday night, June 13**   We've been driving for 2 days. Dad **estimates** that it'll take 2 more days to reach New York. I thought I would be bored stiff during the trip. But there have been lots of surprising things to see as we've driven up the eastern part of the country: gray-green mountains with soaring pine and fir trees, oceans of wildflowers, and lakes that sparkle like jewels. We stopped to look at a waterfall, and behind it was the entrance to a dark, musty cave! Dad wouldn't let us go in there, though. He said he'd have to be crazy as a loon to do *that*.

⁴Later in the day Dad spotted a bald eagle on a telephone pole and slowed down so we could see it. Pretty awesome! Back home, all you see are sparrows and vultures. We saw deer and llamas grazing in a preserve, and some wild turkeys. Of course, we've seen lots of dead animals on the road, too—mostly possums, some raccoons, a couple of birds, and something furry that I couldn't recognize because it was as flat as a tortilla. It could've been a fox.

⁵When Will complained about how long the trip was taking, Mom explained that it was because we were *mee-AN-dur-ing*. Will thought the word meant "misbehaving." That's because he and I almost had a fistfight during a maddening argument about the word "syrup." But Mom spelled it out loud—M-E-A-N-D-E-R-I-N-G—and said that it meant "wandering without a definite plan."

⁶The syrup argument was about how to pronounce the word. Will insists "SUR-up" is the way to say it. I explained that some people call it "SEER-up," and that's okay, too. I told him that it was just like *envelope* and *route* and *caramel*. People in different parts of the country pronounce these words in different ways. Will stubbornly insists that there is one *right* way to say something, and that's *his* way! What do you expect from someone who has a rat for a pet?

[7]**Wednesday morning, June 16**   We arrived in New York last night. We're staying with Mom and Dad's friends. I haven't written in this journal since Sunday, because I started a new book and couldn't put it down. Here are the high points of the last couple of days, though. The scenery continued to be amazing all the way here. I'm a terrible artist, but on the next page, I'll try to **illustrate** the shapes of the trees and hills, so I'll remember how they looked. Dad avoided interstate highways on this trip, because he says you don't see anything when you travel on them. "Yes, you do," Will argued. "You see billboards and fast-food places and gas stations." Dad replied that Will just proved his point.

[8]We've driven on smaller roads and seen lots of small towns and fruit stands. We've seen fields and cattle and broken-down barns. We've crossed wide glistening rivers and small babbling streams. And once, a coal-black snake slithered across the road in front of our car!

[9]Outside a store in Pennsylvania, Will and I heard a man say to another man, "Don't just stand there with your teeth in your mouth, help me with this bicycle tire!" We hadn't heard that expression before. I **interpreted** it to mean the same as "Don't sit there like a bump on a log" or "Make yourself useful." In the car, Will pointed out that the man pronounced *bicycle* "biciggle." "That's not right!" said Mr. Language Expert. Taking a trip through different states is sort of like visiting new countries.

[10]**Wednesday night, June 16**   This city is awesome! I've never seen so many people and buildings. There are unlimited sights to see! We took a ferry to see the Statue of Liberty today. What a powerful statue. I can see why people coming to start new lives in this country wept the first time they saw it. There's a **barrier** that prevents tourists from going inside the statue now. I was disappointed. I wanted to climb to the top and have Dad take a picture of me dangling out of the statue's nose.

[11]We're going to see a play later this week, so we went to the box office and stood in a line to get tickets—except people here say "standing *on* line." Naturally, this amused Will. His ears are constantly being turned by new expressions and pronunciations.

He tries to imitate the way some New Yorkers speak. I always remind him how funny he must sound to them, with his southern accent.

[12]**Thursday night, June 17**   We walked for miles today, and my legs and feet are sore, or as Dad says, "My dogs are yapping." In our hometown, there's not much to see when you take a walk, except houses and convenience stores. But here, you walk among soaring skyscrapers that make you feel like the tiniest ant, and among stores and shops that sell everything in the world—stuff spills out onto the sidewalks from some of the stores— and among gardens and museums and fountains and sidewalk carts with hot dogs and sodas and egg rolls for sale. Will and I couldn't resist the warm, salty smell of fresh soft pretzels. We each bought two!

[13]I started to write "New York is a bustling city," but that's not quite **accurate**. How about "New York is a living, breathing giant that—" Oh, well. I'll think of a good description later.

[14]Oh, yeah—I wanted to remember to write this down: This morning at breakfast we had delicious buttermilk pancakes in a small café. The waiter asked if we wanted any more "SEER-up." Will and I looked at each other and cracked up. Will laughed so hard that he knocked over the little silver syrup pitcher. The gooey stuff spilled all over his new "NYC" T-shirt!

[15]Tomorrow night we're going to an outdoor concert in Central Park. I've heard that this park is huge. The park back home is about as big as a baseball field, but Central Park is probably larger than our whole hometown! We want to visit some museums during the day tomorrow, but we can't yet reach an agreement on which ones to see. New York has history museums, art museums, and even a television and radio museum. To small-town boys like us, this city seems just like heaven!

from Begging for Change

by Sharon G. Flake

Raspberry Hill has seen a lot in her 13 years. Her father is a homeless drug addict. Her hard-working mother has been beaten nearly to death by a young neighbor. But finally Raspberry and her mother are about to move out of their housing project and into a house in Pecan Landings. To celebrate, they are throwing a party. This episode occurs near the end of the novel.

[1]Firecrackers. That's what Odd Job's got in his hands when he knocks on our front door.

[2]"Ain't they illegal?" I ask, picking up a long, skinny red one, and rubbing some of the powder off. "People lose their eyes and fingers all the time with these things."

[3]Odd Job squeezes my nose. "Party pooper," he says, heading for the refrigerator, pulling a tub of no-name ice cream out of a green plastic garbage bag and putting it in the freezer.

[4]"The Fourth of July without fireworks is like cake without ice cream. Useless," he says, heading back out the door and down to the backyard.

[5]I go to my room, open the window and sit on the ledge with my legs hanging out. It's nine o'clock at night, and our party is just getting started. Momma calls it our It's About Time Something Good Happened to Us party, in celebration of the new place we're moving to.

[6]Our yard looks like one of those department store windows. Momma's got red Christmas lights strung along the inside of the wooden fence, circling our tree and twisted around some of the branches. Long thin poles with cups of fire hanging from 'em are stuck in the ground. Red, white, and blue Christmas bulbs are stacked in clear plastic bowls on three tables she borrowed from Miz Evelyn. And all the people who come in get a red, white, or blue shooting star drawn on their cheeks in glitter paint by Ja'nae.

[7]We ain't never had a party before. But people are gonna be talking about this one forever. Momma cooked up a storm. Grilled chicken, burgers, and hot dogs. Made potato salad, fruit salad, and a tuna mold shaped like a cat. Mai's mom brought over egg rolls and fortune cookies. Dr. Mitchell went to the bakery and brought cakes and pies. Me and Ja'nae made lemonade, iced tea, and Kool-Aid. Sato brought over six cans of warm red pop, but I didn't crack on him. It's the thought that counts.

[8]I swing my legs just over my window ledge. Feel the hot air blow over me. Close my eyes and smell the lavender blooming like crazy all over our backyard.

[9]Ming and Ja'nae are sitting by the fence, pointing up at the fireworks that the city just set off. Odd Job is playing spades with his girlfriend Donyell, Momma, Dr. Mitchell, Ming's mom and dad, Su-bok, Ling, and Miz Evelyn from across the street.

[10]Sato and Ling are playing with Couch when Sato points at me and says, "I'm coming up," with Couch following behind.

[11]My bedroom is a mess. You can see dirty socks, jeans, and T-shirts shoved under my bed from when Momma told me to clean up earlier. But I don't try to straighten things now. I reach over, dim the lights, and hope Sato don't trip over nothing.

[12]Couch licks my fingers when I pat his head. Sato sits down next to me. "Man," he says pointing up at the sky, "why can't we have fireworks all

the time?"

¹³I nod my head up and down. I look over at him and see red and white lights in his eyes just when more firecrackers explode way up above us.

¹⁴Sato tells me to move closer to him, then he puts his arm around my shoulder. I look down to see if Momma's watching. She's busy showing Ja'nae her plants. Odd Job's busy telling Dr. Mitchell that he needs to stick to doctoring 'cause he sure can't play no cards, so them two ain't paying me no attention, neither.

¹⁵Sato asks me about Zora. How come she ain't here. I tell him she's at her mom's for the weekend. Her mother's planning a trip to London and Zora gets to go.

¹⁶Sato's sitting so close to me I can't even look up, or I'm gonna be staring right into his nose. So I swallow, then clear my throat, and wonder if my breath stinks.

¹⁷We sit there, stiff as the poles holding the fire in the backyard. Then he leans over and tries to kiss me. I turn away, and ask Couch if he's hungry. "For some ribs or barbecued chicken" I say, rubbing his tail.

¹⁸Sato leans over. "All those flowers your mom planted," he says, pointing around the whole yard, "make it look like your yard don't even belong around here," he says. "Like somebody stole it from Pecan Landings and is hiding it here."

¹⁹My eyes follow his fingers. I smile when I see the row of orange begonias I planted by the fence the other day, and the pink, white, and red rosebushes that been growing like crazy all summer. "That bushy thing that looks like weeds is lavender," I tell him. "And the blue stuff over there crawling all over the fence is morning glory."

²⁰Sato takes my hand and points to a corner of the yard with tall things growing in it. "What's that?" he asks.

²¹But he tricks me, and before I can answer him he kisses me—right on the lips—just like Ming and Ja'nae. I ain't never been kissed before.

²²When I open my eyes, he's staring straight at me.

²³"Your eyes is supposed to be closed," I tell him, kicking my legs out like I'm high up on a swing.

²⁴He's smiling. "Why?"

²⁵"Because."

²⁶"Well, I like mine open," he says, taking his arm from around my shoulder and holding my hand.

²⁷I kick my feet out again. "Who you kissed before?"

²⁸He rubs the little hairs over his lip. "Just you," he says soft and low.

²⁹I feel his fingers cover mine, and his lips get close again. My heart is tick, tick, ticking in my chest. My head is spinning, for real, from the sweet smell coming from the cologne on his neck and the flowers in the yard.

³⁰"Sato! You crazy, boy?" Dr. Mitchell says, just when Sato's soft lips touch mine again.

³¹Sato stares down, then over at me, then down into the yard again.

³²"You! Down here! Now!" Momma says, jumping up from the table. Shaking her fist in the air.

³³Everyone in the whole yard is staring up at us. "Busted!" Ming yells out.

³⁴"Man!" Sato says, helping me off the window ledge and holding my hand all the way to the front door. I stop him in the vestibule. "They gonna jump all over you," I say, talking 'bout Momma, Odd Job, and Dr. Mitchell.

³⁵"That's all right," he says, looking me right in the eyes. "You was worth it."

Connect to the Author

Award-winning writer Sharon G. Flake was born in Pittsburgh, Pennsylvania. Her gritty and realistic novels and short stories deal with issues like prejudice, homelessness, street violence, race, class, and identity. "I really try to write from my gut and feel what other people (my characters) might be feeling," Flake says. "Grown-ups try to tell me more than kids what I should do, and I ignore them. I just think that everybody should know their own stories. What inspired me in terms of young people are young people who tell me that they hated to read or were bad readers, and they liked my work and it made them want to read more, or read somebody else's work. That motivates me to keep writing."

I Love LA!

[1]Have you heard that song by Randy Newman, "I Love LA"? Well, if you've ever visited Los Angeles—like I did recently—you would know why he wrote it. LA is sprawling, thrilling, and a little strange. The possibility of seeing a real, live movie star keeps you excited and alert. The sun spreads like honey over the beaches, hills, and neighborhoods. It warms your spirit. The ocean laps at the edges of the city. It clears the cobwebs in your head. You can't help but feel good walking around in LA. It feels like a place where your dreams could come true.

This LA airport is symbolic of the unique architecture in the city.

[2]In some ways, Los Angeles is its own Disneyland. There are so many different parts of the city that have their own character. Among the strange sights are the Watts Towers. As tall as 10-story buildings, the towers were built from broken bottles, tiles, pebbles, and pottery, with steel rods as a base. They're decorated with thousands of seashells. Weird, huh?

[3]There's a building that looks like a giant pair of binoculars. It was designed by a famous architect. Would it surprise you to know that the building belongs to an advertising company? And there's a record company building that looks like a stack of records, and a fast-food restaurant shaped like a doughnut. This town knows how to have fun with its architecture.

[4]And you've got to love the mixture of people from all over the world. It's not so much a melting pot as a big salad. Someone told me that you'll hear at least 90 different languages spoken by students in LA schools.

[5]Walking along the beach, you see a little bit of everything: muscled guys lifting weights, tanned girls on in-line skates going down the boardwalk, tightrope walkers jumping through hoops on the ropes, a man wearing rainbow-colored hair, and a man dressed like a pirate carrying a parrot on his shoulder. It's like a three-ring circus. Actually, it's more like a six-ring circus.

[6]I stopped to listen to a group of drummers on the beach. Some of the people were playing real drums and others were drumming on plastic buckets and trashcan lids. One member would leave the group and another would step in to take that person's place. Someone said that the circle of drummers goes on and on, all day and sometimes into the night. I hope the residents who live nearby don't mind the sound. Anyway, that's just a small sample of what I saw and heard on the beaches. Like the drummers, the beaches themselves seem to go on and on forever.

[7]You've seen the big, white "Hollywood" sign on TV or in movies, right? Well, I saw the real sign on the hill, from a distance, though. Did you know that the sign is 450 feet long? Don't even *think* about getting close to it. The city has put up cameras and other devices to keep curious visitors from getting near enough to try to climb the letters or otherwise mess with the sign. I have this friend Olly who has always wanted to paint the letters of his name red on the sign. He's going to have to find a new goal in life after I tell him that it's impossible to get near the sign.

[8]Not far from the Hollywood sign is a big park that has miles of trails, picnic grounds, a theater, a nature museum, a zoo, and an observatory where you can gaze at stars—not

Graumans' Chinese Theatre in Hollywood

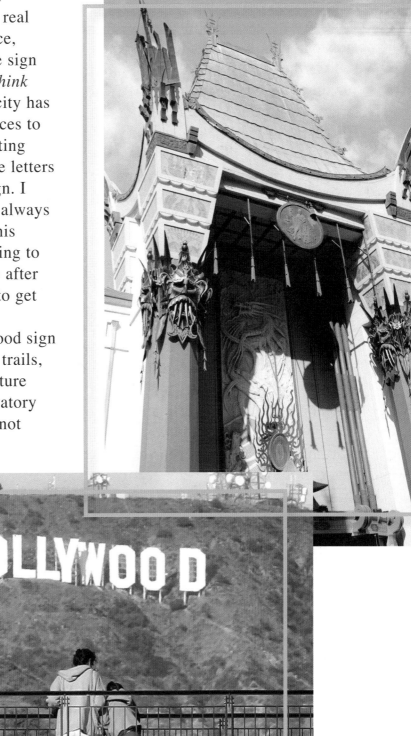

217

movie stars, but the kind in the night sky. You would need about a month to explore the whole park.

[9]And speaking of parks, Disneyland is in south LA. This huge park is just one of several theme parks and other attractions in the area. We spent a long day at Disneyland, from morning till night. Mickey Mouse greeted us, just like you've seen on TV. I had the feeling that a girl, and not a boy, was wearing the Mickey costume, so I asked. I was right. The girl told me that most of the Mickey Mouses are played by girls. The park doesn't want Mickey to look too tall or threatening because that could frighten little children. If you go to Disneyland, be prepared to wait in a lot of lines. About half the world's population was there the day we went.

[10]We also toured Universal Studios, where many movies are made. As we passed the business offices, I imagined big shots making movie deals and saying to each other, "Have your people call my people," and "Let's do lunch." Or film directors in the studio calling out, "Lights, camera, action!" But they didn't show us the business offices or film crews at work. And I didn't see any actors that day, either, except for possibly our guide, who's studying acting in college. The tour was fun, though. The studio is like a complete city, and it's also like a theme park. They take you on a guided, 2-hour tour that includes a collapsing bridge, a flash flood, and an earthquake. Many of these are parts of movie sets from famous films.

[11]Oops, did I say *earthquake*? That's not a favorite word here, where real earthquakes sometimes rumble through the region. Over the years, some of the earthquakes have been deadly and destructive. This area sits atop two huge plates of land that scrape against each other, causing the quakes. The region also has mudslides, forest fires, and floods. Still, millions of people want to live here.

[12]On my last day in LA, I went back to the beach. I took a long walk in the fine sand, which is like light brown sugar. I watched a group of surfers. The waves weren't that big, but they were big enough for the surfers to glide across them for a few glorious seconds. They made surfing look so easy! As I walked, I tried to imagine myself living here. Maybe then I would see movie stars, I thought to myself. Maybe I could *be* a movie star. Why not? This is a place where dreams can come true. I love LA!

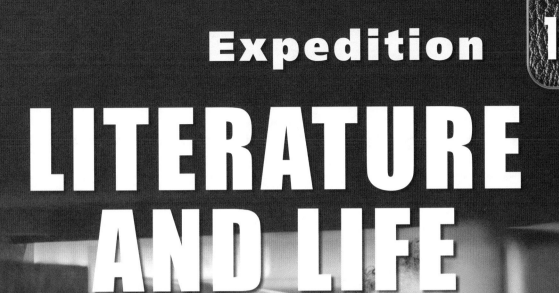

LITERATURE AND LIFE

- *Why do we read stories?*
- *How is the setting important to a story?*
- *How can other people's stories affect us?*

THE STOLEN BICYCLE

by William Saroyan

Ten-year-old Ike George is about to do something completely out of character. The author doesn't say exactly where this story takes place. But it could happen at any time in any urban American neighborhood. It's the kind of neighborhood where you know almost everyone, at least by reputation.

[1]THIS MOVIE OF 1919 was full of high spirits, **recklessness**, and excellent timing, so that when Ike George left the theater he himself was like a man in a movie: full of energy, afraid of nothing, and eager to get on with his life.

[2]As if it were not himself, as if it were not wrong to do so, he took the brand-new bike out of the bicycle rack in front of the theater, and, in full view of the whole world, rode away on it.

[3]Johnny Faragoh, who sold bicycles for Kebo, was standing in front of his house on L Street.

[4]As the boy rode by, Johnny noticed the new bike.

[5]"Hey, kid!" he called out.

[6]The boy turned in the street and coasted up. He knew Johnny. If he called you, you had to stop. It was a pleasure for the boy, though: he had always admired Johnny, who was like somebody in a movie himself.

[7]"That's a swell bike," Johnny said. "Where'd you get it?"

[8]"Mr. York gave it to me for my birthday," the boy said.

[9]"You mean the guy who's in charge of street sales for *The Herald*?"

[10]"Yeah."

[11]The boy got off the bike and let the older one take the handlebars. Johnny lifted the bike, bounced it, sat on it, and very easily began riding around in a small circle.

[12]"He gave you a good one, boy. What's your name?"

[13]"Ike."

[14]"Ike what?"

[15]"Ike George," the boy said.

[16]"You anything to *Cookie* George?"

[17]"He's my cousin."

[18]"First or second?"

[19]"First."

[20]"Cookie's a good friend of mine," Johnny said.

[21]"He's always in trouble," Ike said.

[22]"Where'd you steal it?" Johnny said. "You can tell me."

[23]"I didn't steal it," Ike said. "Mr. York gave it to me for my birthday."

[24]"Cookie's my pal," Johnny said. "Somebody else gave it to you. That guy York wouldn't give you a bike if you saved his life."

[25]"He gave me *this* bike," the boy said.

[26]"Tell them Cookie gave it to you," Johnny said. "Somebody'll go and ask York and you'll get in trouble."

[27]"Cookie's got no money," the boy said.

[28]"Sometimes he has and sometimes he hasn't," Johnny said. "I'm going

to see him tonight," Johnny said. "I'll tell him about it. Go on home now."

²⁹The boy got on the bicycle and rode home.

³⁰When his father saw the bicycle he said, "Haig, where did you get that bicycle?"

³¹"Cookie gave it to me," the boy said.

³²"You mean your cousin Gourken?"

³³"Yes," the boy said. "Gourken has no money," the boy's father said. "You've borrowed it, haven't you?"

³⁴"No," the boy said. "It's mine."

³⁵"Go inside and eat your supper," the father said.

³⁶The boy went inside and ate his supper. It took him less than five minutes. When he came out of the house his father was riding the bike in the yard.

³⁷"Haig," the father said, "take the bicycle back where you got it. You're no thief."

³⁸"Cookie gave it to me," the boy said.

³⁹The next day he rode the bicycle to school, just the way it was. He didn't turn it over and hammer out the numbers the way you were supposed to do. The numbers were 137620R. After school he rode the bicycle to *The Evening Herald*, and told everybody his cousin Cookie had given it to him for a birthday present.

⁴⁰"What's your birthday?" his friend Nick Roma asked him.

⁴¹"September 7, 1909," the boy said.

⁴²"This is May," Nick said. "You'll get in trouble, Ike."

⁴³He rode the bicycle to his corner, Mariposa and Eye, and sold papers all afternoon. Cookie came to the corner in the evening. "Is this the bike?" he said.

⁴⁴"Yeah," the boy said.

⁴⁵"I sure gave you a good one, didn't I?"

⁴⁶"Yeah. Thanks."

⁴⁷By October he had almost forgotten how the bicycle had come into his **possession**. In November the chain broke while he was sprinting. The rim of the front wheel broke and the fork **buckled**. It cost him a dollar-and-a-quarter for a new rim. Another dollar to have the buckled fork replaced by a straight secondhand one, and fifty cents for labor.

[48]After that the bike was his, out and out.

[49]One day a year after he had taken the bike from the rack in front of the Liberty Theater, he put it back into the rack, and went on in and saw the show.

[50]When he came out, the bike was gone. He walked home, and when he saw his father he said, "They stole my bike."

[51]"That's all right," his father said. "Go inside and eat your supper."

[52]"I'm not hungry," the boy said. "If I catch the fellow who stole it, I'll give him the worst beating he ever got."

[53]"Go inside and eat," the boy's father said.

[54]"I don't want to eat," the boy said. He stood before his father, very angry, and then suddenly turned and ran. He ran all the way to town and walked along every street looking for his bike. After an hour he walked home, ate his supper, and went to bed.

[55]He was now eleven years old.

[56]One evening in August he was playing handball with Nick Roma against the wall of the Telephone Building. Nick made a man-killer, a truck turned into the alley, bumped the ball, and carried it down the alley. The boy went after the ball. It had fallen down a small flight of stairs into a narrow passageway where there were garbage cans and boxes full of ashes. He looked for the ball. In a corner he saw a bicycle frame, with the paint scratched off. He turned the frame upside down and read the number. It had been hammered, but he could still read the 13 and the R.

[57]He stood in the dark passageway, holding the old frame. His friend Nick Roma came up and said, "Where's the ball?"

[58]"It's lost," the boy said. "I found my bike. They took everything off of it."

[59]"Is the frame all right?" Nick said.

[60]"It's all right," the boy said, "but what good is a frame without the other stuff?"

[61]"It's worth *something*," Nick said.

[62]"I'd like to get the guy who stole it," the boy said.

[63]Paul Armer came walking down the alley and saw the two boys with the bicycle frame.

[64]He examined the frame with them.

[65]"What do you want for it, Ike?" he said.

[66]"I don't know," the boy said.

[67]He was angry and brokenhearted.

[68]"It was my bike," he said to Paul. "Then they stole it. We were playing handball, I went to get the ball and I found the frame. They took everything off of it and threw it in here."

[69]"Where did the ball go?" Nick said.

[70]"To heck with the ball," Ike said.

[71]"I'll give you a dollar for it," Paul Armer said.

[72]"All right," the boy said.

[73]A week later when he saw the bike again, painted and with new parts, he became angry again and said to himself, "If I ever get the guy who stole it!"

Connect to the Author

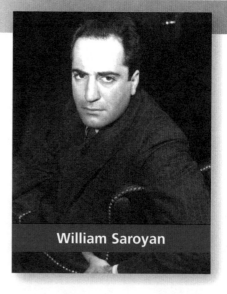

William Saroyan

Born in 1908, William Saroyan would have been about the same age in 1919 as the main character in this story, Ike George. And like Ike, Saroyan sold newspapers to earn money as a boy. It's no coincidence. Saroyan often used his own life and his family as inspiration for his stories. Saroyan was born in Fresno, California, and was the son of Armenian immigrants. When his father died in 1911, Saroyan spent four years in an orphanage. He often got in trouble in school. "I had been kicked out of school so many times that I finally left for good when I was fifteen." Saroyan used writing to help him cope with the sadness of his childhood. "I took to writing at an early age to escape from meaninglessness, uselessness, unimportance, insignificance, poverty, enslavement, ill health, despair, madness, and all manner of other unattractive, natural, and inevitable things." He wrote many short stories, sometimes as many as one a day. He also wrote several novels. But he is best known for his plays, which won him much praise from critics and viewers. Saroyan died of cancer in 1981.

from
The Autobiography of Malcolm X

with the assistance of Alex Haley

Malcolm X was a Black Muslim minister, a militant, a social and political activist, and a hero to many. His journey toward activism began in prison, where he first learned to read with understanding and to write with precision.

[1]It was because of my letters that I happened to stumble upon starting to acquire some kind of a homemade education. I became increasingly frustrated at not being able to express what I wanted to convey in letters that I wrote, especially those to Mr. Elijah Muhammad. In the street, I had been the most **articulate** hustler out there—I had commanded attention when I said something. But now, trying to write simple English, I not only wasn't articulate, I wasn't even **functional**. How would I sound writing in slang, the way I would say it, something such as "Look, daddy, let me pull your coat about cat, Elijah Muhammad—"

[2]Many who today hear me somewhere in person or on television, or those who read something I've said, will think I went to school far beyond the eighth grade. This impression is due entirely to my prison studies.

[3]It had really begun back in the Charlestown Prison, when Bimbi first made me feel envy of his stock of knowledge. Bimbi had always taken charge of any conversations he was in, and I had tried to **emulate** him. But every book I picked up had few sentences which didn't contain anywhere from one to nearly all of the words that might as well have been in Chinese. When I just skipped those words, of course, I really ended up with little idea of what the book said. So I had come to the Norfolk Prison Colony still going through only book-reading motions. Pretty soon, I would have quit even these motions, unless I had received the motivation that I did.

[4]I saw that the best thing I could do was get hold of a dictionary—to study, to learn some words. I was lucky enough to reason also that I should try to improve my penmanship. It was sad. I couldn't even write in a straight line. It was both ideas together that moved me to request a dictionary along with some tablets and pencils from the Norfolk Prison Colony school.

[5]I spent two days just riffling uncertainly through the dictionary's pages. I'd never realized so many words existed! I didn't know *which* words I needed to learn. Finally, just to start some kind of action, I began copying.

[6]In my slow, painstaking, ragged handwriting, I copied into my tablet everything printed on that first page, down to the punctuation marks.

[7]I believe it took me a day. Then, aloud, I read back, to myself, everything I'd written on the tablet. Over and over, aloud, to myself, I read my own handwriting.

[8]I woke up the next morning, thinking about those words—**immensely** proud to realize that not only had I written so much at one time, but I'd written words that I never knew were in the world. Moreover, with a little effort, I also could remember what many of these words meant. I reviewed the words whose meanings I didn't remember. Funny thing, from the dictionary's first page right now, that *aardvark* springs to my mind. The dictionary had a picture of it, a long-tailed, long-eared, burrowing African mammal, which lives off termites caught by sticking out its tongue as an anteater does for ants.

[9]I was so fascinated that I went on—I copied the dictionary's next page. And the same experience came when I studied that. With every succeeding page, I also learned of people and places and events from history. Actually the dictionary is like a miniature encyclopedia. Finally the dictionary's A section had filled a whole tablet—and I went on into the B's. That was the way I started copying what eventually became the entire dictionary. It went a lot faster after so much practice helped me to pick up handwriting speed. Between what I wrote in my tablet, and writing letters, during the rest of my time in prison I would guess I wrote a million words.

[10]I suppose it was **inevitable** that as my word base broadened, I could for the first time pick up a book and read and now begin to understand what the book was saying. Anyone who has read a great deal can imagine the new world that opened. Let me tell you something: from then until I left that prison, in every free moment I had, if I was not reading in the library, I was reading on my bunk. You couldn't have gotten me out of books with a wedge. Between Mr. Muhammad's teachings, my correspondence, my visitors—usually Ella and Reginald—and my reading of books, months passed without my even thinking about being imprisoned. In fact, up to then, I never had been so truly free in my life.

[11]The Norfolk Prison Colony's library was in the school building. A variety of classes was taught there by instructors who came from such places as Harvard and Boston universities. The weekly debates between inmate teams were also held in the school building. You would be astonished to know how worked up convict debaters and audiences would get over subjects like "Should Babies Be Fed Milk?"

[12]Available on the prison library's shelves were books on just about every general subject. Much of the big private collection that Parkhurst had willed to the prison was still in crates and boxes in the back of the library—thousands of old books. Some of them looked ancient: covers faded, old-time parchment-looking binding. Parkhurst, I've mentioned, seemed to have been **principally** interested in history and religion. He had the money and the special interest to have a lot of books that you wouldn't have in general circulation. Any college library would have been lucky to get that collection.

[13]As you can imagine, especially in a prison where there was heavy emphasis on rehabilitation, an inmate was smiled upon if he demonstrated an unusually intense interest in books. There was a sizable number of well-read inmates, especially the popular debaters. Some were said by many to be practically walking encyclopedias. They were almost celebrities. No university would ask any student to devour literature as I did when this new world opened to me, of being able to read and *understand*.

[14]I read more in my room than in the library itself. An inmate who was known to read a lot could check out more than the permitted maximum number of books. I preferred reading in the total isolation of my own room.

[15]When I had progressed to really serious reading, every night at about ten p.m. I would be outraged with the "lights out." It always seemed to catch me right in the middle of something **engrossing**.

[16]Fortunately, right outside my door was a corridor light that cast a glow into my room. The glow was enough to read by, once my eyes adjusted to it. So when "lights out" came, I could sit on the floor where I could continue reading in that glow.

[17]At one-hour intervals the night guards paced past every room. Each time I heard the approaching footstep, I jumped into bed and **feigned** sleep. And as soon as the guard passed, I got back out of bed onto the floor area of that light-glow, where I would read for another fifty-eight minutes—until the guard approached again. That went on until three or four every morning. Three or four hours of sleep a night was enough for me. Often in the years in the streets, I had slept less than that.

Connect to the Author

Malcolm X was born Malcolm Little in 1925. His father, Earl, was a Baptist minister who believed that black and white people should not integrate. The family was harassed by white supremacists, and Malcolm saw his house burned to the ground by the Ku Klux Klan. Soon after, Earl Little was brutally murdered.

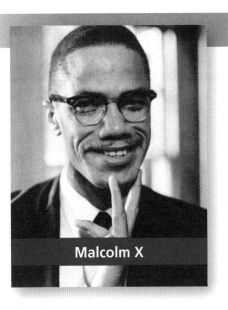

Malcolm X

Perhaps because of these tragedies, Malcolm hoped to become a lawyer. Though he was a good student, his English teacher told him that because of his race, he would never succeed. Shattered by this, Malcolm quit school. He turned to drugs and robbery. He gained a reputation as a smart, tough hustler. Three months before he turned 21 years old, he was sent to prison for burglary. There he continued his drug use and reckless behavior until he met another inmate, Bimbi, who introduced him to the prison library. In prison he learned about the work of Elijah Muhammad. He adopted the name Malcolm X, converted to the Black Muslim faith, and became an outspoken supporter of Elijah Muhammad's Nation of Islam. Elijah Muhammad taught that the only response to racism was for a black man to separate from white society. Malcolm X eventually came to disagree with Elijah Muhammad. He left the Nation of Islam and formed his own group.

Malcolm X was an electrifying speaker and had many followers. However, his popularity made others jealous. He received many death threats. Just before one of his speeches, in 1965, Malcolm X was shot to death. Three Black Muslims were convicted of his murder.

Ruthie's Song

Ms. Emerson thinks that Walt Whitman's poem might change Ruthie's ideas about herself.

Ruthie's teacher gives her a copy of "Song of Myself" from Walt Whitman's most famous book of poetry, Leaves of Grass. *The whole poem is very long. It contains more than 1,300 lines and 52 sections. Ruthie focuses on just a few lines—those that deal with the pressures of society.*

¹The snug, green cap looks ridiculous on Ruthie's head. No matter which way she tilts or turns it, the cap resembles the sort of head covering a patient might wear after a brain operation. "I look like an *idiot!*" she says aloud to her image in the mirror. But she keeps the cap on. Heaving a large sigh, Ruthie sits on her bed and tugs on a pair of clunky red shoes. "What could be sillier than these?" she observes, looking down at the shoes. The term "fashion slave" comes to mind. "So, *this* is how I'm spending my babysitting money," she thinks.

[2]When Ruthie first tried wearing "stylish" clothes, her parents were **baffled**. "I liked the way she dressed before," complained Ruthie's father to his wife. "Why does she want to look like one of the herd all of a sudden?"

[3]"It's a **symptom** of being a teenager," said Ruthie's mother. "Don't say anything to her," she advised. "Perhaps it's just a **phase**. She'll come to her senses." Thus, Ruthie's parents kept their opinions to themselves. With some effort, they managed to avoid showing shock or amusement when Ruthie emerged from her bedroom in tattered overalls or fur-covered boots or other "fashionable" outfits. Sometimes it was difficult, though—as it is this morning when Ruthie appears in the green cap and big shoes.

[4]When she was younger, Ruthie didn't care so much about fitting in. Happily enclosed in the worlds of books and nature, she didn't realize there was an "in" to fit into. She had stories to read and bugs to examine under her **microscope**. But when she turned 13, Ruthie became conscious of the sharp differences between her style and that of the "popular girls." The other girls wore lively, interesting outfits. Until recently, Ruthie wore plain skirts and white blouses. The other girls were bubbling springs of chatter. Ruthie was quiet. The other girls read teen magazines. Ruthie read novels. The other girls flirted with boys. Ruthie just *talked* to boys. She felt left out, invisible, and **abnormal**.

[5]Ruthie's parents aren't the only ones concerned about Ruthie. So is Ms. Emerson, Ruthie's English teacher. Ms. Emerson admires Ruthie's love of reading and her quiet, thoughtful nature. She is curious about Ruthie's attempts to look like the other girls.

[6]One afternoon, when Ruthie is helping Ms. Emerson make photocopies of poems for the class, Ms. Emerson **confronts** Ruthie. "Those silly clothes don't suit you, Ruthie. Why do you wear them?"

[7]Ruthie is surprised by Ms. Emerson's directness. She feels a tightness in her throat as she tries to answer. "I—," Ruthie begins and pauses. "I wanted to try a new way of dressing," she answers weakly. Ms. Emerson continues to look at Ruthie. After a few seconds, Ruthie says, in a quiet voice, "I'm trying to be somebody I'm not. And it's not working."

[8]Ms. Emerson smiles kindly at Ruthie. "Dear girl, you are marvelous just as you are. You should be celebrating who you are. Why would you want to be anything other than that?" And then she hands Ruthie a sheet of paper they had been copying. "Here, read the first three lines," Ms. Emerson directs Ruthie.

[9]Ruthie accepts the sheet of paper. She looks at the poem's title and author—"Song of Myself" by Walt Whitman. Then she reads the lines:

> *I celebrate myself and sing myself,*
> *And what I assume you shall assume,*
> *For every atom belonging to me as good belongs to you.*

Ruthie looks up at Ms. Emerson and smiles. "I like this. It makes me feel happy."

[10]"Take the poem home with you," Ms. Emerson tells Ruthie, handing her the remaining pages of the poem. "It's a long one, but some parts of it may speak to you."

[11]After dinner that night, Ruthie takes the pages out of her backpack. She begins reading the poem. Instead of trying to understand every line, she lets the poem wash over her like a stream. She likes the joyful, vigorous voice of the poet. The poem seems to her a great, long celebration of the essential goodness of the self and of our connection to all others and to nature. Ruthie circles the lines that strike a chord with her. She adds notes in the margins of the paper.

> *Clear and sweet is my soul, and clear and sweet is all that is not my*
> *   soul.*
> "I am fine just as I am. No need to add a green cap."
> *I know I am solid and sound,*
> *To me the converging objects of the universe perpetually flow,*
> *All are written to me, and I must get what the writing means.*
> "My job is to understand the 'writing,' not to try to fit in."
> *I exist as I am, that is enough,*
> *If no other in the world be aware I sit content,*
> *And if each and all be aware I sit content.*
> "I can be happy, whether or not I'm popular."

[12]The next morning, Ruthie's parents—who had so carefully resisted looking shocked at the outfits—look surprised when Ruthie appears in the kitchen. She is wearing a plain brown skirt and a white blouse. Ruthie smiles at her parents but says nothing.

[13]After school that day, Ruthie enters Ms. Emerson's classroom. "I exist

as I am; that is enough!" proclaims Ruthie, adding, "But I'll still want to fit in sometimes."

[14]"Of course. We all feel that way at times. Even Walt Whitman wanted to fit in," says Ms. Emerson. "What we don't realize is that we already do fit in, in a much more important way than belonging to the popular group. Whitman is trying to break through our inability to see how wondrous we are and how connected we are."

[15]Ruthie thanks Ms. Emerson for introducing her to the poem—and to the poet. "I feel as though I've made a new friend in the poet," she says. "And I didn't have to dress up in silly clothes to do it."

Connect to the Author

Walt Whitman was born in Long Island in 1819. By the age of 37, Whitman had worked as a printer and a teacher, had been fired as an editor, and had failed in real estate. He showed little promise. So, many people were surpised when in 1855 he came out with a self-published volume of poems called *Leaves of Grass*. The poems were in a style no one had seen before. Whitman wrote poetry without meter or rhyme. Many readers found it quite unpoetic. But some, like the poet and essayist Ralph Waldo Emerson, thought it was marvelous. He called

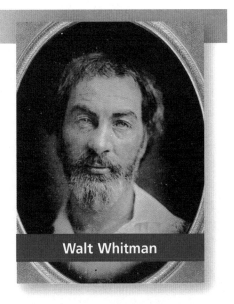

Walt Whitman

Leaves of Grass "the most extraordinary piece of wit and wisdom" America had produced. There were nine editions of the book in Whitman's lifetime. Whitman kept changing the poems—adding or rearranging lines, changing titles, adding or cutting entire poems. During the Civil War, Whitman wrote graphic and moving poems about the horrors he witnessed. In his spare time, he visited wounded soldiers. To cheer them up, he spent his small salary on little gifts for soldiers from both sides. Through his poetry, Whitman became a symbol of the young nation. He wrote about the American experience. He championed the common man. Though he died in 1892, Whitman is still considered one of America's greatest poets.

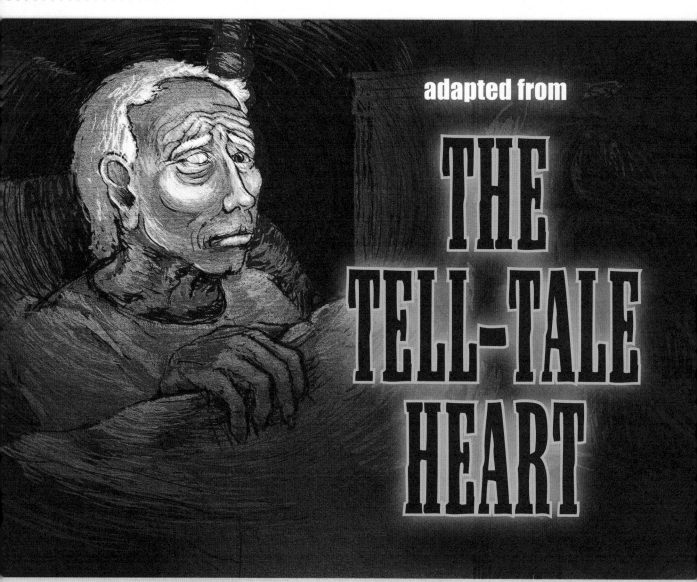

adapted from

THE TELL-TALE HEART

by Edgar Allan Poe

In "The Tell-Tale Heart," we meet a murderer who calmly describes the brutal killing of a harmless, elderly neighbor. The narrator wants us to believe that this horrible deed was not an act of madness. In the end, the killer is driven to confess the crime by the maddening sound of a beating heart. But whose heartbeat is it—that of the narrator, or the murdered man?

The beating of the old man's heart grew louder and louder.

¹I'll admit that I'm a nervous person, dreadfully nervous, but why do you say I'm mad? The nervousness has sharpened my senses, not dulled them. Above all, my sense of hearing is **acute**. I hear many things that others cannot hear, but this is not madness. Listen how **sensibly** and calmly I can tell you the story.

²I cannot say how the idea first occurred to me, but once conceived, it haunted me, day and night. There was no good reason for it. I loved the old man. He hadn't harmed me or insulted me, and I didn't desire his money. I think it was his eye—yes, I *know* it was! One of his eyes resembled a vulture's eye—pale blue, with a film over it. It was worse than an **annoyance**. When the eye looked at me, my blood ran cold. So I decided to kill the man and be rid of the eye forever.

³You think me mad? Could a madman have acted as wisely and cautiously as I did? You should have seen how cunning I was! I was exceptionally kind to the old man the week before I killed him.

⁴Each night, around midnight, I crept into his room, opening the door very carefully. I placed a covered lantern just inside the doorway and then peered into the room, moving the lantern very slowly so I wouldn't wake the man. After **lingering** in the doorway for about an hour, I uncovered part of the lantern so that a thin ray of light shone on the vulture eye. I did this every night for seven nights, but always the Evil Eye was closed, so I could not do my work. Each morning, I went boldly to the man's room and greeted him in hearty tone. He never suspected that I looked in on him every night.

⁵On the eighth night, I was unusually cautious in opening the man's door. Never before had I felt so wise and powerful! The old man had no idea of my deeds or thoughts—I nearly chuckled at the thought—but then, suddenly, he moved on the bed, as if startled. I knew he couldn't see me because the room was black as tar, so I continued moving, steadily, steadily. I was about to uncover the lantern when my thumb slipped on the metal fastener and the man sprang up in bed, crying "Who's there?" I said nothing and stood motionless for a whole hour.

⁶The man sat in bed, listening. Then I heard him utter a groan of mortal terror, a sound I knew well. Many nights, it had welled up from my own chest, increasing my fears. I knew what the old man felt, and pitied him,

although I chuckled at heart. I knew that his fears were growing and that he had been trying to explain them away, likely telling himself "It's nothing but the wind in the chimney." But he comforted himself, in vain, because Death was stalking him. The old man neither saw nor heard me, but I knew that he *felt* my presence.

[7]After a long while, I partially uncovered the lantern. One dim ray, like the thread of a spider, shot from the lantern and fell upon the vulture eye, which was wide open. I grew furious when I saw the dull blue eye with its hideous veil. It chilled me to the bone.

[8]Now, remember: what you mistake for madness is my sharpened senses. I heard a low, dull, quick sound, like the sound of a watch wrapped in cotton. I knew *that* sound well, too. It was the beating of the old man's heart, a sound like a drumbeat that increased my resolve.

> STILL, I REMAINED SILENT AND DID NOT MOVE. I HARDLY BREATHED. I KEPT THE LIGHT FOCUSED ON THE EYE, WHILE THE AWFUL HEARTBEAT GREW QUICKER AND LOUDER EVERY SECOND.

[9]Still, I remained silent and did not move. I hardly breathed. I kept the light focused on the eye, while the awful heartbeat grew quicker and louder every second. How terrified the old man must have been! I told you that I am nervous. At this dead hour of the night, in the terrible silence of the old house, the sound was horrible, yet I remained still. But the beating grew louder and louder until I thought the heart would burst! I feared that a neighbor might hear it. The old man's hour had come!

[10]With a yell, I leaped into the room. The old man shrieked, just once. In an instant, I dragged him to the floor and pressed the mattress onto him. I smiled to know I'd come this far. But the heartbeat continued, muffled, for many minutes. I didn't mind so much, because I knew that it could not be heard through the walls. At last, it ceased. The old man was dead.

[11]I removed the mattress and examined the body: the man was stone dead. I placed my hand over his heart and held it there for many minutes to be sure. He was indeed dead. His eye would trouble me no more.

¹²Do you still think me mad? You won't when you hear how wisely I concealed the corpse. Working hastily, in silence, I cut off the head and arms and legs of the body, and then I removed three of the floorboards and placed the body beneath the floor. I replaced the boards so cleverly that no human eye—not even *his*—could have detected anything irregular. There were no bloodstains, because I had done the dismembering in a tub—ha! ha!

¹³I had just finished my work, around four in the morning, when I heard a knock at the front door. With a light heart—for what did I have to fear, *now?*—I went downstairs and opened the door. Three police officers stood at the door. "A neighbor reported hearing a shriek," one of them said. They had been called to investigate.

¹⁴I smiled and invited them in, for I had nothing to fear. "I was the one who shrieked—a bad dream," I explained. I mentioned that the old man had gone to the country. I bade them search the house, even leading them to the old man's room. Feeling confident from my perfect triumph, I brought in chairs so that we could sit there for a while. I boldly placed my chair over the exact spot where I had buried the body.

¹⁵The officers were satisfied. My *manner* had convinced them. I felt completely at ease. We chatted casually. After a while, though, I began to wish them gone. My head ached and there was a ringing in my ears, but they continued to chat. The ringing became more distinct. To rid myself of the awful feeling, I talked more freely. But the ringing continued, more distinctly, until I noticed that the noise was *not* within my ears.

¹⁶I must've become pale, but I continued to talk, my voice growing louder. Still, the sound increased, *a low, dull, quick sound—like the sound of a watch wrapped in cotton*. I could hardly breathe. The officers seemed not to hear the sound. I talked more excitedly, but the noise only became more **urgent**. I stood and began arguing and gesturing wildly, but the noise grew louder. "Why won't these men leave?" I wondered. I paced back and forth, and still the noise increased. What could I *do*? I raged and swore! I grabbed my chair and grated it on the floorboards, but the noise filled the room and grew louder—*louder*! Still, the men chatted pleasantly, smiling. Surely they were mocking my horror!

237

[17]Anything was better than this agony, anything was better than their scorn. I could **survive** this torment no longer. I would have to scream or die! And now—again—the sound: louder! louder! louder!

[18]"Villains!" I shrieked. "I admit it! Tear up the floorboards! Here, here—it is the beating of his hideous heart!"

Connect to the Author

Edgar Allan Poe was born in Boston in 1809. His father deserted the family, and his mother died when Poe was just an infant. Poe then went to live with a Virginia businessman, John Allan. He attended college for a short time and later served briefly in the army. Around 1827, Poe began writing poems, short stories, and essays. He gained fame with works such as "The Raven," one of the best-known poems in American literature. The modern detective story traces its roots to Poe's dark tales. Despite his fame, Poe was often poor and unhappy. He died in 1849. His stories remain popular more than 150 years after his death.

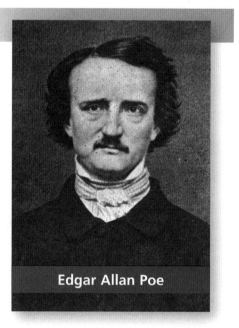

Edgar Allan Poe

The Secret of the Lost Mine

¹The moment the teacher introduced Dan Dobbs to the class, I knew we'd be friends. For one thing, he was the only kid my age in our one-room school. On top of that, I liked how he was friendly and shy at the same time. He didn't like the teacher making a fuss over him, but he smiled and was good natured about it anyway.

[2]After school, Dan always helped his pa pan for gold, but on weekends we hiked into the mountains to hunt and fish. We swapped stories and planned daring adventures. I'd never had a better friend in all my life.

[3]As much as I took to Dan, I didn't much like his pa. Truth is, the steely look in Mr. Dobbs's eyes made me feel he'd just as soon I'd fall down a well. Dan confessed that his pa was what you might call a tough disciplinarian.

[4]"He gave me a fierce whipping for crying as we left St. Louis. I never cry, Willie, really, but I felt just awful about leaving while Ma was away visiting her sister. He didn't even tell her we were going!" Dan shook his head, still unable to believe it himself. "Pa thinks about gold all day and night and doesn't much care about anyone or anything else."

[5]Dan said he'd thought about sneaking away to St. Louis, but he didn't have any money. Besides, he was terrified of what his pa would do if he caught him.

[6]Dan and his pa had been in Jackpot Hills about two months when the robberies began. First, Old Man Parker claimed that his gold had been stolen out of his saddlebag. Two weeks later, Jim Baker's gold was stolen out from under his cabin. Not long after that, Buckskin Charlie announced that his famous gold nugget, the biggest one ever found in Jackpot, had disappeared. People started getting jittery. There had been plenty of squabbles over claims and such in Jackpot Hills, but no one had ever stooped to thieving before.

[7]Around that time, Dan seemed quieter than usual. After the first robbery, he missed school, and when I asked if he'd been sick, all he said was "not exactly." The same thing happened after Baker was robbed. I hated to think Dan would steal, but I knew that gold could buy a stage coach ticket back to St. Louis, and a whole lot more.

[8]The morning after Buckskin Charlie got robbed, I skipped school and hid near Dan's place. When he came out, I followed him into the mountains. After about an hour, Dan stopped by a pile of leaves and pushed them aside. Then he lifted an old board

and disappeared underground. It was the Lost Mine! Years ago, a miner had bragged about striking gold up in the mountains, but then he disappeared. Folks never knew whether he'd died in his mine or just moved on, and no one had ever found the mine—until now!

⁹After a few minutes, Dan came back out and headed home. I stayed as still as a stone until he was out of sight, then I ran to the mine. Near the entrance, I found some matches and lit a candle Dan had stashed away. I crawled into the cool, damp darkness and soon found a compartment dug into the wall of the mine tunnel. I reached in and pulled out a flour sack containing two small bags of gold and one large gold nugget. My heart sank. Dan was a thief! I knew why he needed money, but thieving is thieving.

¹⁰Just then, I heard the crunch of boots on the gravel so I grabbed the sack, crawled further into the mine, and blew out the candle. My heart pounded like thunder as Dan's dark profile appeared at the entrance.

¹¹"Dan," I said nervously. "It's me, Willie, and I found the gold."

¹²Dan hesitated, then whispered, "I can't explain now because Pa is after me and he's angry. I've got to hide."

¹³The picture of an angry Mr. Dobbs started me trembling. "Bring the matches," I said. Dan crawled to me and lit the candle.

¹⁴"I've never gone far into this tunnel for fear it might cave in," he said, "but I think we'd better take our chances." He led the way and I followed.

¹⁵From a distance Mr. Dobbs yelled, "Boy, I'll have your hide if you don't bring me what's mine right now!"

¹⁶Suddenly, it all made sense—Mr. Dobbs had stolen the gold!

Dan spoke softly, "Willie, I wanted to return it, I swear. I just wasn't sure how to do it without landing Pa in jail." Mr. Dobbs called out again, but this time he was much closer.

¹⁷"We'll figure it out," I whispered. "Right now, we'd better find a hiding place." We crawled deeper into the mine, but there was no place to hide. Suddenly, Dan dropped the candle and blackness surrounded us. I began breathing hard, panicking at the thought of a cave-in.

[18]Just then, Mr. Dobbs hollered into the mine. "So here's your hideaway, you little traitor. Hand over that gold or I'll roll boulders in and start a cave-in easy as pie."

[19]"He'll do it!" Dan whispered. "We'd better go out and take our lickin'." I was sure a cave-in couldn't be worse than facing Mr. Dobbs, so I kept going. "Hey!" I whispered. "There's a light!"

[20]Off to our right was a dim ray of sunlight. We felt our way into a side tunnel and crawled toward it.

[21]"I'm warning you—Bring me that gold right now or I'll dig it out of your dead hands later!" Mr. Dobbs's voice was closer. He was inside the tunnel!

[22]When we reached the light, we saw that it came through an opening that was too small to fit through, so we started clawing at the dirt to make it larger. Rocks and earth showered down from the roof of the mine. Just as the side tunnel began to collapse, Dan pushed me up through the hole. Then I reached back and pulled him out.

[23]As the ground sank in a snaking pattern that followed the tunnel, dust billowed up from the mine entrance and the hole we'd climbed through. Stunned and silent, we realized that Mr. Dobbs was never coming out of that mine. Tears of shock and grief sprang from Dan's eyes. At the same time, his shoulders slumped forward with relief.

[24]It didn't take long for Dan to straighten things out. He returned the gold to its rightful owners, and they all pitched in and gave him a reward. It was just enough for his ticket home.

[25]I miss Dan something awful, but we send letters often. We're planning an adventure for next summer, but there's one thing we've agreed on—this one will be a little less dangerous than our adventure in the Lost Mine!

UNCOMMON HEROES

- *What challenges do people face in the work they do?*
- *How can the work you do make a difference in the world?*
- *What work are you inspired to do in your life?*

Mother Jones:
The Most Dangerous Woman in America

"I belong to a class which has been robbed, exploited, and plundered down through many long centuries. And because I belong to that class, I have an impulse to go and help break the chains."

—Mother Jones

Mother Jones was a champion of organized labor from the 1870s to her death in 1930.

[1]Mary Harris Jones was called Mother by the men, women, and children whose rights she fought for. She was already 41 years old when she set aside personal tragedy and took up the cause of American workers, young and old. The more popular she became, the more her enemies fought her. She was arrested often. She was jailed at least four times. And she spent four months in **solitary** confinement. But though she lived to be 100 years old, she never gave up the fight.

[2]Mary Harris was born in Ireland in 1830. Her parents rented land from a rich landowner. Her father worked for him as a hired hand. When Mary was five years old, her father got in trouble for joining an **uprising** against

the hated landlords. He fled Ireland to the United States. His family joined him in New York when Mary was 11 years old. Soon after, they followed him to Toronto, where he found work on the railroads. Mary's parents could barely read or write. But schools in Canada were free, and Mary's parents made sure their children got an education. Mary was the first in her family to graduate from high school.

³Just before the start of the Civil War, Mary moved to Memphis, Tennessee, where she found a teaching job. She married George Jones, an iron worker and union organizer. Unions are groups of workers who band together to protect workers' rights. Mary and George had four children. They lived in comfort until 1867. That year, the dreaded Yellow Fever swept through Memphis. The fever killed George and all four children. **Devastated**, Mary left Memphis and moved to Chicago. She found work sewing curtains and clothes for rich people. The contrast between the wealth of her employers and the poverty that surrounded her made a deep impression on Mary. Then came the second great tragedy of her life: the great Chicago fire of 1871. It destroyed one-sixth of the city. Like so many others in Chicago, Mary lost everything she owned. While the rich could recover, Mary wondered what would happen to the poor.

⁴Walking through the ruined city one night, Mary came across a meeting of a secret workers' group. They were called the Knights of Labor. They proposed joint ownership of property as the solution to the problems of the poor. She joined on the spot. It was the beginning of her career as a labor organizer. She became frustrated with the group's slow progress and eventually quit. But Mary worked the rest of her long life to help poor workers and their families.

⁵By the 1890s, newspaper stories followed Mary—known widely by then as "Mother" Jones—while she fought **verbal** battles across the country. She was drawn particularly to the problems facing the men and children who worked in coal mines. They worked 12- and 14-hour days for very low wages. Workers had to pay these wages back to the mine owners for rent and food. Because of this, workers were always in debt. And the work was very dangerous. Many miners died when mines collapsed or exploded. Mother Jones's solution, at mines all across the country, was to organize workers to strike—or quit working—until the mine bosses improved conditions. To **rally** workers, she gave fiery speeches sprinkled with rough language and humor. When mine owners hired guards to break up strikes with violence, this old

woman would stand before them and dare them to shoot her. Her enemies began to call her "the most dangerous woman in America."

[6]When she was 82 years old, Mother Jones spoke to striking coal miners in Cabin Creek, West Virginia. At the time, West Virginia miners suffered the highest rate of death in the country. She **condemned** mine owners for the conditions in which they kept the workers: "They wouldn't keep their dog where they keep you fellows. You know that."

[7]Standing in front of hundreds of workers and their families, she described one way the mine owners took advantage of workers:

[8]I want to show you here that the average wages you fellows get in this country is $500 a year. Before you get a thing to eat, there is $20 taken out a month, which leaves about $24 a month. Then you go to the 'pluck-me' stores and want to get something to eat for your wife, and you are off that day, and the child comes back and says, "Papa, I can't get anything."

[9]"Why?" he says. "There is $4 coming to me."

[10]The child says, "They said there was nothing coming to you." And the child goes back crying without a mouthful of anything to eat. The father goes to the 'pluck-me' store and says to the manager, "There is $4 coming to me," and the manager says, "Oh, no, we have kept that for rent. You are charged $6 a month, and there are only three days gone, and there is a rule that two-thirds of the rent is to be kept even if there is only one day."

[11]That is honesty? Do you wonder [why] these women starve? Do you wonder at this uprising? And you fellows have stood it entirely too long! It is time now to put a stop to it! We will give the Governor until tomorrow night to take them guards out of Cabin Creek.

[12]When she reached the age of 90, Mother Jones had to slow down. She had little money and no home. But she had many friends. She went to live with a retired miner and his wife in Maryland. On her 100th birthday, Mother Jones gave her last speech. Listeners said it was as powerful as any she had given. She died seven months later. More than 4,000 mine workers and thousands of others came to her funeral. They wanted to say good-bye to the woman who had fought for them—the woman they called Mother Jones.

A Letter from the Mine

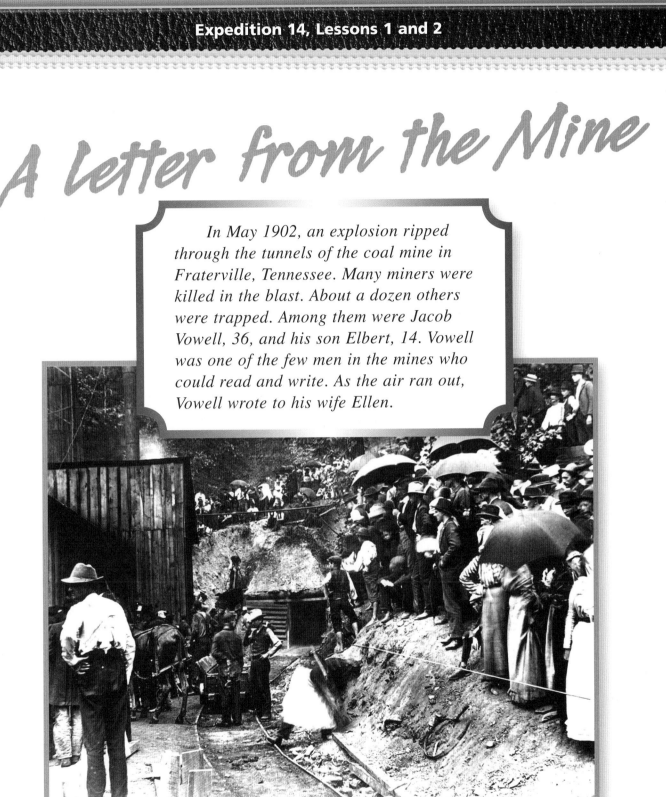

In May 1902, an explosion ripped through the tunnels of the coal mine in Fraterville, Tennessee. Many miners were killed in the blast. About a dozen others were trapped. Among them were Jacob Vowell, 36, and his son Elbert, 14. Vowell was one of the few men in the mines who could read and write. As the air ran out, Vowell wrote to his wife Ellen.

People gather outside the Fraterville coal mine near Lake City, Tennessee. On May 19, 1902, more than 200 men and boys perished.

¹³**T**o My Wife: We are shut up at the head of the entry with a little air and the bad air is closing in on us fast and it is now about 12 o'clock. Dear Ellen, I have to leave you in a bad condition. But dear wife, set your trust in the Lord to help you raise my little children. Ellen, take care of my little darling Lilly. Ellen, little Elbert said that he had trusted in the Lord. Charley Woods said that he was saved if he never lived to see the outside again, he would meet his mother in heaven. If we never live to get out we are not hurt, but only **perishing** for air. There is but a few of us here and I don't know where the other men is.

¹⁴We are all praying for air to support us but it is getting so bad without any. Horace, Elbert said for you to wear his shoes and clothing. It is now past 1.

¹⁵Oh! How I wish to be with you. Good Bye all of you. Good Bye. Bury me and Elbert in the same grave by Little Eddy. Good Bye Ellen. Good Bye Lilly. Good Bye Jimmie. Good Bye Minnie. Good Bye Horace. We are together. It is 25 minutes after Two. There is a few of us alive yet.

¹⁶Oh God, for one more breath. Ellen remember me as long as you live. Good Bye Darling.
Jacob Vowell

Postscript
More than 200 miners died in the tragedy. In the entire town of Fraterville, only three men were left alive. They were the only men not in the mine at the time. The disaster left about 1,000 children without fathers.

A Young Miner's Day

August 5, 1903

¹⁷**I** got up late this morning. It was past 4 a.m. So by the time I ate and did my chores and walked the 4 miles to the mine, I had missed the mantrip. That's the cart that takes miners to the coal seam. We're working deep inside the mountain now. The main tunnel is about 5 feet tall, just big

enough for a boy or a mule to walk upright. But deeper inside the mine, the tunnels are lower. Some are 4 feet high. Some are only 3 feet. So I had to walk, bent over, with all my tools and my lunch pail, for 3 miles to reach the seam of coal.

[18]Most of the fellows here can't read or write. Since I can, I could probably get a better job, if there was any to be had. But there ain't. So me and Daddy and Luther and Everett work in the mines, like everyone else around here. We get 17 cents for every ton of coal we pull out of this mountain. Working together, me and Luther can usually mine 5 tons in a day.

[19]The workday lasts 10 hours, from the darkness of morning until the dark of night. It seems our whole lives are spent in darkness. We wear lanterns on our hats with open flames. But the light is weak and barely **penetrates** the blackness around us. Gases seep out of veins in the rocks. The air is foul and sometimes poisonous. It pools deep within the earth and sometimes, when it touches the flames of our lights, it explodes. Those explosions are powerful. I heard that in Tennessee, an explosion drove a plank of wood through a mule and into the rock, pinning the animal to the ceiling.

[20]It is frightfully noisy work. The mules pull steel carts full of coal, and the wheels clatter against the rock. But the old-timers, the men in their 30s, don't seem to notice the noise anymore. It is filthy, too. We squat or kneel in the mud and swing our picks at the black veins of coal that snake through the stone. Black coal dust covers everything—walls, mules, people. It burrows deep into your skin so that no amount of washing will get it all out of your pores. It seeps into your lungs and will eventually kill you. I just hope I can find somewhere else to work at before that happens to me.

from *Gig*:
Americans Talk About Their Jobs

Merchandise Handler Janice Lejeune

To create the book Gig, *interviewers sat down with several dozen Americans and asked them about their jobs. They taped the interviews, transcribed them, and then cut them down to create personal essays. In this essay, Janice Lejeune describes her job at J.C. Penney. (Sign language was interpreted by Glenda Langlinais.)*

¹I work in the stockroom at J.C. Penney's in Lafayette, Louisiana. I'm a merchandise-handler-slash-prep associate. Which means I do a couple of different things. I use the price gun to add the price tags to clothing. I hang up clothes. And I do something—it's a little bit like doing the price tag but you don't use a gun. It's a different thing. I'm not really sure what it's called. I put on the security tags to prevent people from stealing the clothing. I sort some of the clothing onto the shelves. I work with getting more cartons. And then I bring the empty cartons to be cut up.

²I'm forty-eight years old. I was born deaf. And I have a condition called Usher's Syndrome. Most people who have it are born with normal vision and then later on in their lives they develop tunnel vision and their vision starts to get smaller and smaller. When I was about thirty-seven or thirty-eight, my vision started to get a lot smaller, and it started to become blurrier until it just faded away. So right now I have no vision whatsoever—well, I can see if somebody might turn on a light maybe. But that's it. So to communicate I'm using **tactile** signing where I'm actually having to hold on to people's hands when they sign to me. So I can feel them making the signs.

³I've been working here for two and a half years. It's the first real job I've ever had in my life. Before this, I was a housewife. Things didn't work out with my husband and I—and I was really sad that we got divorced. We had been married for twenty-one years. After he divorced me I was living on Social Security money. I didn't like that. My children were getting older, they'd gone off to college. I was by myself. I felt very lonely. I couldn't really afford to pay my bills plus food, transportation.

⁴So I was living in Baton Rouge, and I decided to go through a training program for disabled people. I went to Little Rock, Arkansas, for an evaluation, and then I went up to New York and got some training and I

worked a little bit in a cigar box factory in an **evaluation** program, and then I came here to Lafayette to the Affiliated Blind of Louisiana. They trained me to be more independent. I learned better communications skills, transportation skills, and whatnot.

[5]After my training, I was going to go back to Baton Rouge and start working there. But I decided to settle in Lafayette instead because Lafayette, I felt like—not catered—but was much more accessible to people with deaf-blindness. There's a lot of people here who have the same kind of condition that I do. I felt like that would be a good support system for me.

[6]So I stayed, but then I went to different places for eleven months, looking for a job with no luck. I was very nervous because I had never worked before and I thought I would never find anything. In the end, J.C. Penney hired me because the **personnel** director, her cousin—actually two of her cousins—have the same type of blindness that I have. They're both deaf and going blind just like I am. So she knew that people with deaf-blindness could work. And that was a great advantage. And I was hired on.

[7]I really enjoy my job. I like it because it's something that I can do with my hands. It's easy for someone like me to do, and I can do it continuously. It's not complicated. It's not dangerous. I stay in an immediate area. I'm not having to walk from this point to that point to that point. I know where to go and I don't have to get lost or be afraid that there might be danger. It's very smooth.

[8]And the people here are so nice. When I first started, there was one time I got lost, and I was wandering all over the place for a long time, and I kind of yelled out loud and someone came, a salesgirl, and she was able to guide me to where I was going, you know, and I was safe. It wasn't a big problem. Now, if there's a complication or a problem or things are mixed up, I just holler out and then someone will come and help me. Like say the price tags on top of a box need to be changed to go with a particular item and I don't have the vision to do that, somebody might come and change those tags for me and maybe tell me, "This goes here and this goes there."

[9]It's not like I have a lot of problems at work, though. I'm not saying that. Most of the time, I'm very organized—everything has a place and I'm used to things being in their place. But it's just nice the way they treat me. They're caring. They're very caring. They seem to be very sensitive to my

needs. They'll come to me, and they might show me things or touch my hand, you know? And I'll smile and say hi and they'll say hi and we might print on palm for a little bit. Generally, I can identify people by the jewelry that they wear; say it's a ring that they wear, I can tell that. So they come by just very short—we might do short, simple gesturing—it's nice. And then I go on with my job.

[10]I'm always motivated to work. J.C. Penney's is a wonderful place to work at. It never gets old and boring for me. I feel that I am ambitious at my job. And I'm very focused. I really feel other people, you know, might work at a slower pace than I do. They like to talk. My boss said that those people are always taking their time and talking. But, of course, I can't sit there and gossip and talk to my neighbors or whatever so I'm more focused on what I'm doing at hand. So I am quick on my job. My boss says that he likes me and wants me to stay working here.

[11]The only thing is, I'm disappointed it's only part-time. It's twenty hours a week, sometimes with overtime. I'd like full-time. I'd like benefits. I get no benefits whatsoever. I've been talking with my boss and my supervisor, saying, you know, I would really love to have benefits. Can you increase my hours just a little bit? And they say no, maybe later on. Maybe later

on. Maybe in the future. But J.C. Penney's, it's their policy not to give the workers full-time. So I don't know. I'm studying to get my GED degree. When I'm finished, I'd like to get an advanced job maybe, or a promotion. I will work full-time somewhere. That's what I'm really looking for. I want to work. I think having a job is good for people—especially someone with a disability. It gives you a goal, something to get up and look forward to in the mornings and it gives you things to do. Without anything to do, I think you get more closed-minded. You feel more and more like there's not anything you can do. It hurts your self-esteem. Working is wonderful for your self-esteem.

[12]My condition, I know that it's hard, but I've grown up knowing that this is what I've had. It wasn't like a whole new situation that I didn't know what to do in. And you know I couldn't say, oh, well, I don't want to accept this. I had to say, okay, I can do this, I can use a cane, I can use tactile signing and just accept the way I am in my life with this.

[13]Now I'm getting used to it more, and I'm adapting more to it. It's still hard, but I feel successful. Which is just a very nice way to feel. Because, you know, like I said, I hadn't worked all that time before this. Then I came here, and those people were looking at me, to see what I could do, how I would work out. I was like a **representation** of deaf-blind people. And I've been showing them what we can do.

Connect to the Author

About 40 interviewers contributed to *Gig*. One of the interviewers was John Bowe, who also is an editor of the book. Bowe traveled around the country talking to a wide variety of people, including a carnival worker in Appalachia, a supermodel between flights at an airport, and truck drivers at a truck stop in Wyoming. The editors of the book wanted Americans to speak for themselves. "Our goal was to take accurate snapshots, person by person, of work as it is today in this country," writes Marisa Bowe, John's sister and another of the book's editors. "We were very moved by the wholehearted diligence people bring to their work."

Helen Keller: Author, Lecturer, Social Reformer

Helen Keller, 12, with her teacher Anne Sullivan in 1892

Like Janice Lejeune, Helen Keller was unable to see or hear. Left blind and deaf as the result of a childhood illness, Keller overcame these obstacles. She provided people of all abilities a model for leading a successful and meaningful life.

In the following quotations, Keller reveals something about her early struggles. The time line summarizes important events throughout Keller's life.

On the illness that caused her to lose sight and hearing:
"They called it acute congestion of the stomach, and the fever left me as suddenly and mysteriously as it had come. There was great rejoicing in the family that morning, but none, not even the doctor, knew that I should never see or hear again."

On her frustration at being unable to see or hear:
"Sometimes I stood between two persons who were conversing and touched their lips. I could not understand, and was **vexed**. I moved my lips and **gesticulated** frantically without result. This made me so angry at times that I kicked and screamed until I was exhausted."

On discovering how to communicate:
"My teacher and I walked down the path to the well-house, attracted by the fragrance of the honeysuckle with which it was covered. Someone was drawing water and my teacher placed my hand under the spout. As the cool stream gushed over one hand, she spelled into the other the word 'water,' first slowly, then rapidly. I stood still, my whole attention fixed upon the motions of her fingers. Suddenly I felt a misty consciousness as of something forgotten—a thrill of returning thought; and somehow the mystery of language was revealed to me. I knew that 'w-a-t-e-r' meant the wonderful cool something that was flowing over my hand. That living word awakened my soul, gave it light, hope, joy, set it free! There were barriers still, it is true, but barriers that could in time be swept away."

This Alabama quarter features an image of Helen Keller and is the first circulating coin in the U.S. to contain Braille. Keller's name is printed in Braille and in English.

Helen Keller Time Line

1880
Helen Adams Keller is born on June 27 in the small rural town of Tuscumbia, Alabama. She is a healthy baby, and able to see and hear.

1882
When she is 19 months old, Helen becomes extremely ill. The illness renders her deaf and blind.

1886
Alexander Graham Bell, the inventor of the telephone and an expert on deafness, examines Helen and recommends she have a teacher.

1887
On March 3, teacher Anne Mansfield Sullivan, age 20, arrives from the Perkins Institution for the Blind in Boston. Sullivan, who had been blind, regained some of her sight through surgery.

1887
On April 5, at the water pump in the yard, Helen understands for the first time the connection between an object and the word that Anne Sullivan signs into her hand. Helen's parents call it a miracle.

1888
On a trip to the Northeast, Helen meets President Grover Cleveland.

1890
Around this time, Helen resolves to learn to speak. She eventually is able to speak English, French, and German.

1894
She attends school in New York City. There she works on her speaking skills. She sharpens her skills through reading lips and placing her hands over the speaker's mouth.

1899
Keller passes the admissions test for Radcliffe College.

1900
Keller enters Radcliffe College; Sullivan accompanies her to every class, except on test days.

1903
Still a sophomore in college, she writes *The Story of My Life.*

Around this time, Keller also serves on the Massachusetts State Commission on the Welfare of the Blind.

1904
Keller graduates with honors from Radcliffe College.

1905
Keller becomes the first person to write openly about blindness in babies for newspapers and national magazines.

1910
Keller publishes *The Song of the Stone Wall,* a book of poems.

1913
She works as a reporter for United Press International.

1914
Keller leaves with Sullivan on her first international speaking tour.

1929
Keller writes *Midstream: My Later Life.*

1930
Anne Sullivan becomes blind. Keller founds the Helen Keller Endowment Fund for the American Foundation for the Blind.

1936
Anne Sullivan dies. Helen Keller is awarded the Theodore Roosevelt Distinguished Service Medal.

1941–1945
Keller works with soldiers blinded during World War II.

1955
To honor Anne Sullivan, Keller writes the biography *Teacher.*

Author Helen Keller, who is blind and deaf, is photographed holding an open Braille book in January 1955.

1964
President Lyndon Johnson awards Keller the Presidential Medal of Freedom, America's highest civilian honor.

1968
On June 1, Keller dies in her sleep in Connecticut.

Ali Defies Critics,
Challenges Berbick for Title

Heavyweight boxer Muhammad Ali makes a point during a news conference.

December 11, 1981

[1]NASSAU, Bahamas—Tonight Muhammad Ali will try to take the title of world heavyweight champion for a record fourth time. Ali was the first boxer ever to win the title three times. Ali failed to take the title from Larry Holmes last year. Holmes embarrassed Ali in a bloody battle that had to be stopped by the referee. Many say that fight showed that Ali is past his prime. Critics say he has no business challenging the likes of Trevor Berbick. Ali insists he will prevail. "All those who don't think I can make it, watch," says the Champ. "Watch me return!" Ali has already made his place in history. So why risk another loss and possible injury? Ali says it's for the same reason that people go to the moon. "Because it's there."

[2]Cynics say he's simply after the money. It's true that Ali's name can make even a bad match a **commercial** success. But the Champ says he has

plenty of **revenue** these days. He insists that money is not what matters to him at this point.

[3]". . . the main thing in my idea of coming back is to go down in history. Regardless of how much money I get, nothing can buy history. To be four-time champion is greater than all the money in the world to me."

[4]History gives Ali good reason to think he can prove the critics wrong and win. The odds were not in his favor when he took up boxing at the age of 12. The son of a sign painter and a housekeeper in the segregated South had little reason to hope for fame and glory. But that didn't stop him from boxing his way up through the ranks to win the gold medal at the 1960 Olympics. Tunney Hunsaker was the first to fight Ali when he turned pro. At that time, Ali was still known as Cassius Clay. Hunsaker expected to beat the inexperienced Clay easily. But the young fighter surprised him.

[5]"He was fast as lightning and could hit from any position without getting hit," said Hunsaker after losing the fight. He predicted that Cassius Clay would someday become the heavyweight champion of the world.

[6]In those days, the quips that have now become **staples** of Ali's press conferences were considered rude and cocky. Many people were put off when he bragged that he was "the Greatest" and able to "float like a butterfly" and "sting like a bee." Boxing experts mistook his unusual moves for poor form. **Traditional** fighters kept their fists up and bobbed up and down or side to side. But Ali didn't seem to know how to fight properly. He held his hands low and backed away from punches. Only after he took the world heavyweight title from Sonny Liston did critics begin to respect Ali's style and personality.

[7]Ali was one of the most unusual boxers ever to come on the scene. He moved and talked like no other fighter ever had. He dominated the sport for years and seemed to be fearless. Many disliked his stand against military service in the Vietnam War, but few would dispute the courage it took to stick to his beliefs. Ali's refusal to fight in the war cost him his title and his right to box. But that didn't weaken his principles. Ali accepted the consequences, though he thought they were unfair. When he was allowed to fight again, he didn't demand his title back. He just got into the ring and won it back, like a true champion. After historic losses to Frazier, Norton, and Spinks, Ali came back to beat each of them in rematches. That is how a great

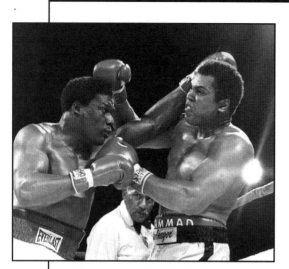

Muhammad Ali, right, takes a punch from Canadian Trevor Berbick during the first round of their 10-round bout in Nassau, Bahamas.

fighter ignores the odds and wins three world championships.

[8]So why don't critics believe Ali can come back to win a fourth title tonight? For one thing, Ali is almost 40 years old. His opponent is a tough young fighter in his prime. And the Holmes fight made it clear that the Champ's reactions have slowed down dramatically. Even Ali admits that his coordination isn't what it used to be. There is also a worrisome slur in his speech. This is likely a sign of damage from too many hard blows. All these factors weigh heavily against Ali. His fans can only hope that tonight will not bring a repeat of humiliation that Ali suffered in the Holmes fight.

Career Highlights

1959–60
National Golden Gloves amateur boxing champion

1960
Wins Olympic gold medal for light-heavyweight boxing

1960
In his first pro fight defeats Tunney Hunsaker

1964
Defeats Sonny Liston to win world heavyweight title
Announces he is Muslim and adopts the name Muhammad Ali

1965
Scores a first-round knockout in a rematch against Liston

1967
On April 28, as a conscientious objector, refuses to serve in the Vietnam War

1967
On April 29, stripped of championship title by World Boxing Association

1967
On June 20, found guilty of draft evasion; sentenced to five years in prison, but remains free on appeal

1970
Allowed to resume boxing

1971
Loses to Joe Frazier in New York on March 8

1971
On June 28, draft-evasion conviction reversed by U.S. Supreme Court

1974
Knocks out favorite George Foreman to regain the world heavyweight title

1975
Defeats Joe Frazier with a 14th-round knockout

1978
Loses heavyweight title to Leon Spinks on February 15

1978
On September 15, beats Spinks to win the world heavyweight title for a record third time

1979
Announces his retirement from boxing

1980
Returns to the ring and loses to Larry Holmes

1981
Loses to Trevor Berbick; retires with a pro career record of 56-5, including 37 knockouts

The Golden Years of a Champion

Muhammad Ali arrives at Singapore's airport in 2005. Ali has fans all over the world.

[9]Muhammad Ali, three-time heavyweight champion of the world, is recognized as one of the greatest boxers in history. Today, he has left behind his Golden Gloves and has entered his golden years. After retiring in 1981, Ali left the boxing ring but not the spotlight. He has traveled the world. He has met the leaders of many countries. He has continued to reach out to his fans through talk shows and public appearances. When Ali lit the Olympic flame in Atlanta in 1996, the cheers of the crowd showed how much he is still admired by fans all over the world.

In a 2001 radio interview with Juan Williams, Ali described his life after boxing:

> **Williams:** What's Muhammad Ali like at age 60?
>
> **Ali:** I'm the same person, a little more settled. A little more cool and calm. Not as fast as I was. That's about all.
>
> **Williams:** I read where you said that you are fighting now for peace. Fighting against racism. Fighting for literacy. This means all the boxing was just a prelude to what you do now.
>
> **Ali:** You not as dumb as you look.
>
> **Williams:** Well thank you, Ali. (laughs)
>
> **Ali:** No, boxing was a . . . I used it as a method to get famous first. Then I could use the fame to promote certain causes.

[10]One way Ali is working to promote good causes is through the United Nations. He is a UN Messenger of Peace. Ali's job is to visit countries where he can encourage reforms and support programs for children and the poor.

[11]Ali also has gotten leaders at home to take action on issues that matter to him. One of those issues is boxing. To help reform boxing, Ali appeared before the Senate committee that oversees **commerce**. He pointed out abuses in the boxing world that should be stopped. Congress later passed the Muhammad Ali Boxing Reform Act. The law protects boxers from injury and from unfair treatment by managers. Ali appeared before another Senate subcommittee to address a completely different issue. He asked that Congress increase funding for research on Parkinson's Disease. Parkinson's is the disease that causes Ali's soft, slurred speech and the trembling in his hands.

[12]The Muhammad Ali Center is another of Ali's worthy projects. It is a large meeting place in the Champ's hometown of Louisville, Kentucky. The center is a gathering place for groups from all countries, races, and religions. People meet there to promote peace and understanding. Programs at the center are filmed for **distribution** to schools and youth groups. Ali hopes that the center will carry on his legacy of service and peace.

[13]Working to promote these causes is what matters most to Muhammad Ali now. In a recent biography, he described the spiritual turn his life has taken: "My main goal now is helping people and preparing for the hereafter. I'm working harder now than I ever did in boxing."

No League of Their Own

photo by Don Hays

by Dan Silverman

In the 1940s, as more and more young men were drafted to fight in World War II, team owners became concerned that Major League Baseball parks would go bankrupt for lack of players. In response, a group of businessmen founded the All-American Girls Professional Baseball League. But just as in the men's teams (until Jackie Robinson broke the color barrier in 1947), only whites were allowed to play. Black men had formed the Negro Leagues so they could play. Three talented black women also found a home there.

Permission courtesy of Mamie Johnson assisted by Tony Dee

Mamie "Peanut" Johnson leaped to fame with her talent and skill among her fellow male players.

[1]There's a scene in the movie, *A League of Their Own*, about the birth of the All-American Girls Professional Baseball League during World War II, when the ball gets away from the players on the field. It stops near an African American woman, who was not participating in the action. She picks it up and whips it back in, the ball popping impressively into the mitt of one of the players.

[2]The moment was a **poignant** reminder, during an otherwise uplifting story, that this unique opportunity was not available for African Americans. Not that the league, which lasted from 1943–54, had any written rules against it.

[3]"The people I've spoken to didn't blame the absence of black players on prejudice," said Bill Madden, author of *The All-American Girls Professional Baseball League Record Book*. "More than one person I interviewed told me they just weren't up to speed. They said black women at the time weren't really involved in softball, which is where they got most of their players."

[4]"We had a few blacks try out, but they just weren't as good," said Carl Winsch, manager of the league's South Bend Blue Sox from 1951–54. But after some consideration, he admitted, "If the league tried harder, shook the bushes more, as we used to say, we might've come up with someone."

[5]That someone could've been Mamie "Peanut" Johnson. In fact, the black woman in the movie was intended to represent Johnson, who attended a league tryout in Alexandria, Virginia, in the early 1950s.

[6]"I showed up with a friend of mine, Rita Jones," said Johnson. "They looked at me like I was crazy. They never even let me try out."

[7]Instead, Johnson would go on to play in the Negro Leagues—with the men. She was actually one of three known women of the era to play in the League, along with Toni Stone and Connie Morgan.

[8]Stone was the first of the three to make it. After barnstorming with minor league teams in the late 1940s, she was signed by the Indianapolis Clowns in 1953 to replace a second baseman named Hank Aaron, who had left to play in the Major Leagues. As Aaron and some of the other black superstars trickled into the Majors, the Negro Leagues were forced to look for new gate attractions.

[9]"Truly, the **incentive** was to get fans," said Ray Doswell, curator of the Negro Leagues Museum in Kansas City. "But it's not like they could get just anyone off the street. They found a real athlete in Toni Stone."

[10]Negro League statistics were not as efficiently **compiled** as were those of the Major Leagues, but according to James Riley's *The Biographical Encyclopedia of the Negro Baseball Leagues*, Stone batted a respectable .243 her first season, which included a hit off legendary pitcher Satchel Paige.

[11]"Paige was so good that he'd ask batters where they wanted it, just so they'd have a chance," said Stone before she died in 1996. "So I get up there and he says, 'Hey, T, how do you like it?' And I said, 'It doesn't matter, just don't hurt me.' When he wound up—he had these big old feet—all you could see was his shoe. I stood there shaking, but I got a hit. Right out over second base. Happiest moment in my life."

[12]Stone was traded to the Kansas City Monarchs after 50 games, and was replaced by another woman, 19-year-old Connie Morgan.

[13]"Morgan was another great athlete," said Doswell. "She played several sports, including basketball, in the offseason."

[14]But the ace of this trio had to be Johnson. While Stone and Morgan both played second base, Johnson, who joined the Clowns as a starting pitcher in 1953, was part of the regular rotation.

[15]"I pitched every six days or so," said Johnson. "Sometimes I went nine innings, other times six or seven."

[16]And how did she do?

[17]"I struck out my share."

[18]One victim, who played for the Birmingham Black Barons, was particularly memorable.

[19]"He said I wasn't as big as a peanut, how'd I expect to strike anyone out," said Johnson. And how did he fare against her? "Oh, I struck him out."

[20]Though the nickname "Peanut" stuck, **resentment** toward Johnson did not. For the most part, the rest of the players wholeheartedly accepted her.

[21]"The men I played with were complete gentlemen," emphasized Johnson.

[22]Says Doswell, who has witnessed firsthand how Johnson is received during Negro League reunions, "Mamie Johnson is just like one of the guys."

[23]That fact was quite evident last year in Queens, New York, during a Negro League Conference at LaGuardia Community College. Johnson took her place at the dais with other former Negro League players: Bob Scott, Jim Robinson, and Lionel Evelyn. She fit right in, reminiscing with the fellas about playing ball as a kid, talking about her favorite baseball memories, **bemoaning** the modern player's lack of a sense of history.

[24]But among the audience, Johnson clearly stood out. Few people were familiar with former Negro Leaguers beyond a handful of superstars. Even fewer were aware that women played—and held their own—alongside some of these legends of the game. But there sat "Peanut" Johnson, a living testament to a fascinating piece of baseball history.

[25]A typical "Peanut" moment came when Bruce Brooks, the moderator of the event and a professor at LaGuardia (as well as a professional baseball fan) asked about a well-known story that claims Satchel Paige taught Johnson how to throw a curveball. Johnson, however, showed mock **indignation** at the suggestion that she needed such advice. "He didn't teach me how to throw it, he taught me how to perfect it," corrected Johnson. "I knew how to throw it."

[26]And throw it she did. During three seasons, some records show Johnson with an overall 33-8 mark.

[27]While she has nothing but positive memories about her playing days— "Have you ever won a million dollars?" she responded to a question about how she looks back on her time in the Negro Leagues—Johnson does have some strong opinions about today's players.

[28]"I don't think they realize, or understand, that if it weren't for these gentlemen," said Johnson, referring to her fellow panel members, "for Mr. Robinson, for Mr. Banks, Mr. Aaron, Mr. Mays, then they wouldn't be where they are today."

[29]Johnson left the Negro Leagues in 1955—"I had a young son, and it was time for me to come home"—and pursued a career in nursing for more than 30 years. But she has never really left the game. She runs the Negro League Baseball Shop with her son, Gary, in Maryland.

[30]Clearly, baseball has remained a part of Mamie "Peanut" Johnson's soul.

[31]"Those were the three best years of my life," said Johnson. "Just to know I was good enough to be there was a tremendous thing for me.

[32]If they didn't let me play, I wouldn't be who I am today, and I'm very proud of that."

Scratching Out a Living

[1]**Y**ou probably have never heard of Richard Quitevis. But if you're a fan of hip hop music and culture, you might know Richard by his other name: DJ Q-Bert. The DJ part stands for disc jockey, the person who plays the music that others dance to at parties and clubs. But Q-Bert does more than just play other people's music. He uses old-fashioned vinyl records and a record player to turn other people's music into something completely different. This skill is called "turntablism," after the turntable that spins the record on the record player. Q-Bert has been called "the Michael Jordan of turntablism."

1969

Richard Quitevis
born in Daly
City, California

1985

Starts scratching
records on a
turntable

1991

Becomes world
champion at
international DJ
contest

[2]Records are how people listened to music before compact discs and MP3s. A record holds recorded music in a long groove that spirals from the outside edge to the center. A record player has a turntable and a pivoting arm with a needle at one end. This needle is set into the beginning of the groove. As the turntable spins, the needle is dragged across tiny ridges in the groove. This causes the needle to vibrate. The record player turns these vibrations into sounds. When the record spins at the right speed in one direction, the result is music.

[3]Some people weren't interested in the music made by records spinning slowly in one direction. They discovered that they could make scratchy noises by using their hands to move the record back and forth rapidly. Soon people were calling this new method of making music "scratching." They found, also, that by moving the record in different ways, they could produce different noises. And with a lot of practice, they could arrange these new noises in ways that sounded like a whole new song.

Becoming Q-Bert

[4]Richard Quitevis was born in 1969 in Daly City, California. He started scratching records as a teenager in 1985. "At first, I was scratching for fun and because I thought it sounded good," he says. "But a couple of months later, I realized that the turntables were a musical instrument, and my

1995

Forms a band with a group of other DJs, including Mix Master Mike, who later joined the Beastie Boys

1998

Inducted into DJ Hall of Fame; releases Wave Twisters, an album of original scratch music

2000

Wave Twisters released as an animated movie

techniques were evolving every day, like a kung fu fighter or jazz artist." Richard and a group of his friends practiced for hours in his bedroom. During their practice sessions, they learned new techniques by listening to hip hop records and watching each other perform. They also adopted hip hop names. That's when Richard became DJ Q-Bert.

[5]Soon Q-Bert and his friends were scratching at parties and talent shows. Before long, they were entering DJ contests called "battles" and testing their skills against top DJs. Q-Bert began to develop a reputation as one of the fastest and most talented scratchers around. Eventually, Q-Bert was winning DJ battles. Then, in 1991, he won the world's biggest DJ battle. He was the world champion. He kept winning contests until, in 1998, he was voted into the DJ Hall of Fame.

[6]Q-Bert no longer battles other DJs in competitions, but he still practices every day. "I love scratching and working to better myself in the areas that I love," he says. "I'm always doing shows and performing, so in a sense, that's like battling. I always want to be better than my last performance. I guess I'm battling myself to get better."

[7]Q-Bert says scratching is his way of communicating. "Music to me is like language," he says. "I hear something I like, then translate that into scratching. I'll hear, for instance, the way a girl sings, then take the aspects of that and lay that into my scratching. Let's say she sang very soft and gracefully. I'll go to the tables and get a kind of soft, girlish-sounding voice, scratch it, and make sure it's soft and graceful."

269

Spreading the Word

[8]Many people don't think that turntablists are real musicians. Q-Bert disagrees. "With any art, there comes hardcore training to get to that higher level of expertise, and the same goes for scratching on turntables," he says. To him, it takes as much skill to make music with a turntable as it does to make music with a guitar. "The turntable is a musical instrument in that sense," he says. "How many different things can you do on a guitar? It's just infinity. Your imagination is your limit to how many tricks or how many ways you have of doing things."

[9]Today, Q-Bert travels the world performing his amazing turntable music. But the thing that makes him happiest is sharing his knowledge with aspiring turntablists. "I do love to give advice to people who want to learn from the things I know, since I've been doing it for a pretty long while," he says. "But I love to learn from them equally. I don't feel above anyone, because we all know something more than the next guy."

[10]Q-Bert helps the next generation of turntablists by making DVDs that teach scratching skills. His advice to aspiring DJs is, "Practice, practice, then practice again. Be easy on yourself, but not too easy." He also urges newcomers to find their own personal style. "In the beginning it's like a child copying the elders," he says. "But in time you will develop your own personality. So just stick with it and you will be rewarded."

[11]To help aspiring DJs practice, Q-Bert worked with a company to invent a new turntable called the QFO. It's shaped like a flying saucer and can run on solar power. Now DJs can take their turntables anywhere to practice, just like guitar players. "I go to the beach out here a lot, and I always see a lot of guys playing guitar and bongos on the beach," he says. "I was wondering how I could scratch out here at the beach so I invented the QFO thing. Now I can take it out there and practice."

[12]And, as you know, practice makes perfect.

THE REAL ME

- **How are we shaped by our childhood experiences?**
- **How do advertisements try to sell us an image?**
- **What different qualities help define who you are?**

from
Barrio Boy
by Ernesto Galarza

From 1910 to 1920, Mexico was torn apart by a bloody revolution. Hundreds of thousands of Mexicans fled to the United States to find safety and work. Among them were young Ernesto Galarza and his family. They left their small village and settled in Sacramento, California. In this excerpt from Galarza's autobiography, Ernesto's mother, Henriqueta, enrolls him in school. Neither six-year-old Ernesto nor his mother speaks English.

[1]The two of us walked south on Fifth Street one morning to the corner of Q Street and turned right. Half of the block was occupied by the Lincoln School. It was a three-story wooden building, with two wings that gave it the shape of a double-T connected by a central hall. It was a new building, painted yellow, with a shingled roof that was not like the red tile of the school in Mazatlán. I noticed other differences, none of them very reassuring.

[2]We walked up the wide staircase hand in hand and through the door, which closed by itself. . .

272

³Exactly as we had been told, there was a sign on the door in both Spanish and English: "Principal." We crossed the hall and entered the office of Miss Nettie Hopley.

⁴Miss Hopley was at a roll-top desk to one side, sitting in a swivel chair that moved on wheels. There was a sofa against the opposite wall, flanked by two windows and a door that opened on a small balcony. Chairs were set around a table and framed pictures hung on the walls of a man with long white hair and another with a sad face and a black beard.

⁵The principal half turned in the swivel chair to look at us over the pinch glasses crossed on the ridge of her nose. To do this she had to duck her head slightly as if she were about to step through a low doorway.

⁶What Miss Hopley said to us we did not know, but we saw in her eyes a warm welcome, and when she took off her glasses and straightened up she smiled wholeheartedly, like Mrs. Dodson. We were, of course, saying nothing, only catching the friendliness of her voice and the sparkle in her eyes while she said words we did not understand. She signaled us to the table. Almost tiptoeing across the office, I **maneuvered** myself to keep my mother between me and the gringo lady. In a matter of seconds I had to decide whether she was a possible friend or a **menace**. We sat down.

⁷Then Miss Hopley did a **formidable** thing. She stood up. Had she been standing when we entered she would have seemed tall. But rising from her chair she soared. And what she carried up and up with her was a buxom superstructure, firm shoulders, a straight sharp nose, full cheeks slightly molded by a curved line along the nostrils, thin lips that moved like steel springs, and a high forehead topped by hair gathered in a bun. Miss Hopley was not a giant in body but when she mobilized it to a standing position she seemed a match for giants. I decided I liked her.

⁸She strode to a door in the far corner of the office, opened it and called a name. A boy of about ten years appeared in the doorway. He sat down at one end of the table. He was brown like us, a plump kid with shiny black hair combed straight back, neat, cool, and faintly obnoxious.

⁹Miss Hopley joined us with a large book and some papers in her hand. She, too, sat down and the questions and answers began by way of our interpreter. . .

¹⁰As long as the questions continued, Doña Henriqueta could stay and I was secure. Now that they were over, Miss Hopley saw her to the door,

dismissed our interpreter and without further ado took me by the hand and strode down the hall to Miss Ryan's first grade.

[11]Miss Ryan took me to a seat at the front of the room, into which I shrank—the better to survey her. She was, to skinny, somewhat runty me, of a withering height when she patrolled the class. And when I least expected it, there she was, crouching by my desk, her blond **radiant** face level with mine, her voice patiently maneuvering me over the awful idiocies of the English language.

[12]During the next few weeks Miss Ryan overcame my fears of tall energetic teachers as she bent over my desk to help me with a word in the pre-primer. Step by step, she loosened me and my classmates from the safe **anchorage** of the desks for recitations at the blackboard and consultations at her desk. Frequently she burst into happy announcements to the whole class. "Ito can read a sentence," and small Japanese Ito, squint-eyed and shy, slowly read aloud while the class listened in wonder: "Come, Skipper, come. Come and run." The Korean, Portuguese, Italian, and Polish first-graders had similar moments of glory, no less shining than mine the day I conquered "butterfly," which I had been **persistently** pronouncing in standard Spanish as boo-ter-flee. "Children," Miss Ryan called for attention. "Ernesto has learned how to pronounce *butterfly*!" And I proved it with a perfect imitation of Miss Ryan. From that celebrated success, I was soon able to match Ito's progress as a sentence reader with "Come, butterfly, come fly with me." ...

[13]Like the first grade, the rest of the Lincoln School was a sampling of the lower part of town where many races made their home. My pals in the second grade were Kazushi, whose parents spoke only Japanese; Matti, a skinny Italian boy; and Manuel, a fat Portuguese who would never get into a fight but wrestled you to the ground and just sat on you. Our assortment of nationalities included Koreans, Yugoslavs, Poles, Irish, and home-grown Americans.

[14]Miss Hopley and her teachers never let us forget why we were at Lincoln: for those who were alien, to become good Americans; for those who were so born, to accept the rest of us. Off the school grounds we traded the same insults we heard from our elders. On the playground we were sure to be marched up to the principal's office for calling someone a wop, a

chink, a dago, or a greaser. The school was not so much a melting pot as a griddle where Miss Hopley and her helpers warmed knowledge into us and roasted racial hatreds out of us.

[15]At Lincoln, making us into Americans did not mean scrubbing away what made us originally foreign. The teachers called us as our parents did, or as close as they could pronounce our names in Spanish or Japanese. No one was ever scolded or punished for speaking in his native tongue on the playground. Matti told the class about his mother's down quilt, which she had made in Italy with the fine feathers of a thousand geese. Encarnación acted out how boys learned to fish in the Philippines. I astounded the third grade with the story of my travels on a stagecoach, which nobody else in the class had seen except in the museum at Sutter's Fort. After a visit to the Crocker Art Gallery and its collection of heroic paintings of the golden age of California, someone showed a silk scroll with a Chinese painting. Miss Hopley herself had a way of expressing wonder over these matters before a class, her eyes wide open until they popped slightly. It was easy for me to feel that becoming a proud American, as she said we should, did not mean feeling ashamed of being a Mexican.

Connect to the Author

Ernesto Galarza was born in 1905 in a tiny mountain village in western Mexico. After his family settled in Sacramento, Galarza quickly learned English and did very well in school. In the summers, Galarza earned money as a farm worker, picking fruits and vegetables. He eventually won a scholarship to college. After earning advanced degrees from Stanford and Columbia universities, Galarza returned to Sacramento. There he helped farm workers fight unjust working conditions. He led strikes against growers and helped organize workers into unions. Galarza retired from union work in the 1960s. He taught school and devoted himself to community work. He also wrote many books for young readers. Galarza died in 1984.

TOY STORY

¹**H**ere's an amazing fact: kids love to play with toys. Okay, well, maybe that's not so amazing. What is surprising these days is what you notice when you look at the *types* of toys that children play with. In this era of equal opportunity for women, girls still play with dolls and boys still play with trucks. Fifty years ago, women were expected to be homemakers. Now their choices are limitless. They can be presidents of corporations or jet pilots. They can be computer programmers or firefighters. **Despite** this change, toymakers continue to create "boy toys" and "girl toys." And **merchants** continue to sell them. We're limiting children's choices and supporting outdated ideas. It's time to do something about this. Let's stop buying toys that are targeted to boys or to girls. It's that simple.

²Why can't a girl play with a truck? Why can't a boy play with a doll? It's partly due to our culture. And it's largely due to producers of children's toys. A recent study shows that children as young as 18 months of age associate pictures of dolls with girls and pictures of trucks with boys. Toy companies claim they're creating more toys that can be played with by both girls and

boys. When you browse toy store shelves, though, you see that toymakers are still operating in the dark ages. These days our society is more conscious of "gender stereotyping." (This is a fancy term for holding on to a fixed idea about supposed differences between girls and boys.) So why are toy companies lagging behind?

[3]Some people think that children are "hardwired" to prefer certain types of toys. Not long ago, a researcher studied monkeys as they played with toys. She found that the monkeys' toy preferences were much like those of human children. Male monkeys spent more time playing with "boy toys" such as cars and balls. Female monkeys spent more time playing with "girl toys" such as dolls and kitchen items. The male and female monkeys spent roughly the same amount of time with toys such as stuffed animals and picture books. Perhaps we are born with certain preferences. Even so, there's no doubt that toymakers build on these preferences.

[4]Toymakers and advertisers spend millions of dollars to influence buyers' habits. In spite of what they may claim, they're still making "girl toys" and "boy toys." How do we know? Come with us on a visit to the girls' section of a large toy store. This section is easy to find: just look for the color pink. The shelves are filled with dolls, dollhouses, kitchen sets, purses, makeup kits, stuffed animals, and toy sewing machines. We counted more than a dozen toys with the word *princess* on them. What's the message here? "Girls are mainly interested in fashion and homemaking."

[5]Fifty years ago, the girls' section of a toy store was similarly stocked. Not much has changed in half a century! And, just as she was 50 years ago, Barbie is still a top seller. In the early Barbie years—the 1960s—stores sold only the doll and her ever-expanding wardrobe. Now they feature complete play sets. You can buy a dollhouse-sized mall complex where Barbie and her friends can shop. It even comes with tiny gold credit cards!

[6]In spite of this, there *are* some small glimmers of hope on today's "girl-toy" shelves. You'll now find Lego sets in both the girls' and boys' sections. The blocks for girls come in "softer" colors, such as lavender and pink, than those for boys, though. You can buy "Soccer Barbie," although she still has the same impossibly proportioned body and big hair. And there are now video games on the "girl-toy" shelves. They come in pink boxes with princesses or Barbies on them. We even spotted a construction set for girls. It has a shopping theme.

[7]Compared with the girls' section, the boys' section of the toy store is a lot louder. Follow the sounds of engines, fake gunfire, beeps, and blips to find this section. As in the past, the shelves are crammed with cars, trucks, trains, toy weapons, tool sets, robots, and action figures such as GI Joe. (He's been around almost as long as Barbie.) Unlike earlier years, though, the "boy-toy" shelves are full of action video games. Also in contrast to earlier times, today's "boy toys" are more complicated. And, of course, there are more tech-oriented toys for boys than for girls.

[8]Some smaller toy stores don't have separate sections for girls and boys. Still, it's not hard to tell which toys are targeted to which gender. Just look at the packaging. The chart that accompanies this editorial is based on a survey of toddler toys. Do you think the parents of a 2-year-old girl will be persuaded to buy the train set that shows a boy on the package?

[9]So, if traditional male and female roles are changing, why are toymakers still promoting these roles for males and females? What's the **advantage** for them? Researchers Fern Johnson and Karren Young studied the marketing of toys. They concluded that it is "more profitable for producers of children's toys to create separate toys for boys and girls as a way of placing more items in the marketplace." More types of toys mean more money for toy companies.

[10]Television advertisers play a part in this, too. Their job is to persuade children as to what toys they should want to play with. The type of voice heard in an ad and the choice of words can send a **definite** message. Action figures and electronic games are clearly marketed to boys. Dolls and animals are aimed at girls. Does a toy have the word *power* in its name? It's likely promoting a "boy toy." Does the ad use a high-pitched or melodic female voice? It's likely promoting a "girl toy." The ads send the messages of "this is how boys act" and "this is how girls act."

[11]Toys serve an important **function** for children. They're tools in a child's learning process. Through toys, children discover themselves and the world around them. We should be more **concerned** about the messages we're sending through the toys we offer children. If a toy sends a message that boys are always tough and girls are always gentle, then children are ill prepared for adult life. If your son wants to play with a doll or a kitchen set, or your

daughter wants to play with a football or a dump truck, that's fine. So, let's put pressure on toymakers to stop making "girl toys" and "boy toys." We should never limit children's horizons. Instead, let's teach them to celebrate who they are and who they can be through the toy choices they make.

Girl Toy or Boy Toy?
What Do the Images on the Packaging Suggest?

Number of girls and/or boys shown on packaging of typical toddler toys		
Toy	**Number of girls**	**Number of boys**
Discover Sounds Kitchen	1	1
Discover Sounds Workshop	0	3
Little Handiworker	0	1
Cast 'n Fishing Set	0	1
Choo-Choo Train	0	1
Racin' Rider RC Cycle	0	1
Rock and Scoot Zebra	1	2
Easy Store Activity Zoo	1	2
Rocking Horse	1	1
Musical instruments (piano, drum, xylophone, rhythm maker)	1	1
Toddle Tots School Bus	0	1
Electronic Project Workshop	1	1
Piggy Bank	0	0

from DUNK

by David Lubar

Amid the amusement park thrills on the boardwalk in Atlantic City, Chad is mesmerized by the guy in the dunk tank. He represents everything Chad is not. With 11th grade just a summer away, Chad is walking the line between being a boy and becoming a man.

[1]**H**is voice ripped the air like a chain saw. The harsh cry sliced straight through my guts the first time I heard it. The sound cut deep, but the words cut deeper. He shredded any fool who wandered near the cage. He drove people wild. He drove them crazy. Best of all, he drove them to blow wads of cash for a chance to plunge him into a tank of slimy water.

[2]This was just about the coolest thing I'd ever seen. Which made it that much more amazing since I lived in one of the coolest places on the planet and I'd seen some of the freakiest things man or nature had ever created.

[3]I was on my way down the boardwalk to get a slice of pizza at Salvatore's. Today was the start of the tourist season. The crowds were thin because the ocean water was still chilly. That wouldn't last. In a few weeks the place would be mobbed. It would stay that way until the end of summer—wall-to-wall tourists frantically packing as much activity as possible into their vacation at the Jersey shore. I hoped someone special would also return. But if I thought about her too much right now, I knew I'd go crazy.

[4]Thin crowds or not, a dozen people had gathered near the tank, watching, listening, laughing at the marks. That's what you call someone who's about to play a game—a mark. Or a vic, which is short for victim. I'd seen dunk tanks before, but I'd never paid much attention to them. Not until now.

[5]The whole tank wasn't more than five feet wide and maybe eight feet high. The bottom half was filled with water, the top half was protected by iron bars. The protection was *definitely* necessary. A shelf on a hinge ran along the back wall. A metal target attached to a lever stuck out from the left side of the booth. The other end of the lever supported the shelf. Behind the target, a large sheet of canvas hung from a wire stretched between two poles. A wooden sign in front of the cage simply said:

DUNK THE BOZO
3 BALLS FOR $2

[6]That pretty much explained the object of the game.

[7]Ten feet in front of the cage, a guy with a change apron—a barker—sold balls to the players. This barker didn't have to do much barking—the game sold itself. I edged closer but stayed behind the crowd so I wouldn't attract the Bozo's attention. I shouldn't have worried. He wouldn't waste his breath on some kid who looked like he didn't have more than five bucks in his pocket. What would be the point in that? He sure wasn't there because he liked falling into a pool of bacteria soup. He was there to rake in the dollars.

[8]"Hey!" the Bozo shouted at a guy near the front of the small crowd. "Where'd you get that wig? You scalp it off a poodle?"

[9]The crowd laughed and the guy's face turned the color of a bad sunburn. His right hand jerked up toward his head, as if he wanted to adjust the fake hair that was plastered there.

[10]"Yeah, you," the Bozo shouted, pointing straight at the guy, turning himself into a nightmare version of an Uncle Sam poster. "What's the matter? Did you get glue in your ears when you pasted on that wig?"

[11]The mark yanked his wallet from his pocket and whipped out a couple bucks. The barker traded the money for three baseballs he'd grabbed from a plastic five-gallon bucket at his feet. He did all this with one hand while holding a half-eaten hot dog in the other. I noticed mustard and ketchup smeared on the change apron tied over his belt. Crumbs littered the front of his shirt and dangled from the shaggy fringe of his mustache, making me think of snowflakes on a pine branch.

[12]"Imagine that," the Bozo said, his voice growing less harsh as he spoke to the crowd. It was almost like he was sharing a secret with us. "Somewhere there's a poor dog running around with a bare behind so this guy can have a curly head. Woof, woof."

[13]"Oof," the mark grunted as he threw the first ball.

[14]*Thwunk!* The ball smacked the large sheet of canvas, missing the target by at least a foot. The back of the mark's neck grew even redder.

[15]"Hhhhhaaaaawwwwhhhooooooheeeeeeeyyaaaa!" The Bozo leaned close to the microphone that hung from the top of the cage and let loose with a screaming laugh, another chain saw through my guts. "If that's your best throw, you'd better just mail the other balls to me. Anybody got a stamp?" His grin was amplified by a huge red smile. He wore a clown's face—white

forehead and cheeks, black stars around the eyes, red painted nose. Like most clowns, he was scary as heck.

¹⁶*Thwunk!* Ball two. Nothing but canvas. It sounded like a pro wrestler getting body slammed.

¹⁷"If I had your arm, I'd trade it for a leg," the Bozo screamed. "Hhhhhaa aaawwwwhhhoooooheeeeeeeyyaaaa!"

¹⁸Above us, a flock of circling sea gulls squawked in agreement.

¹⁹The mark, his face as red as the Bozo's nose, hurled the last ball so hard he nearly fell over. I could feel my own shoulder muscles burning in sympathy.

²⁰*Thaaaaawunnnk!* I jumped back as the baseball smacked the canvas. A couple people chuckled, but most of the crowd murmured sounds of sympathy. They were beginning to root for this clumsy David to luck out and drown Goliath.

²¹I braced for the laugh, but the Bozo surprised me. "Aw, shucks," he said, quietly. "That was really close. I was sure you had me that time." He looked down for a moment, as if he'd lost interest in the guy. Then, before the mark was even two steps away, the Bozo snapped his head back up and shouted, "Loooooooserrrrrrrrrrrrrrrrrrrrr!"

²²The word stretched out like a cheap motorcycle engine stuck in first gear.

²³I couldn't believe it. The mark spun back so fast, I thought his wig would fly off. His hand was already digging for his wallet. He wasn't a person anymore—he was a puppet. The Bozo had control.

²⁴The guy missed again with all three balls. Before the last ball had even stopped rolling, he'd bought another round. This time his third throw nicked the edge of the target, but not hard enough to trip the lever under the Bozo's seat. The crowd let out a sigh of disappointment.

²⁵The poor vic went through twelve dollars before he finally nailed the target, sending the Bozo plunging into the water. It caught me by surprise. He'd missed so many times, I figured he'd never score.

²⁶"So there," the mark said as he strutted away, smirking. Amazing—he'd just blown more money than a lot of people make in an hour, and he was leaving empty-handed. No prize of any kind. But he still acted like a winner.

²⁷In less than a blink, the Bozo lifted the platform, locked it in place, and

scampered back to his seat. He reminded me of a seal slithering out of a pool. As he flicked his head to the side, throwing a shower of water from his hair, I realized he'd already picked his next vic.

[28]"Hey, lady," he said, staring at a woman who was laughing at him. "I may be wet, but you're funny looking. And tomorrow, guess what? I'll be dry."

[29]He paused for an instant as the crowd grew quiet, then added, "Yeah, I'll be dry, and you'll still be funny looking. Haaaaaahhooeeee!"

[30]*Thwunk.*

[31]*Thwunk.*

[32]*Thwunk.*

[33]She did better than the guy. It only took her eight bucks to get satisfaction and revenge. She walked away with a dark smile.

[34]Not me.

[35]My shoes might as well have been nailed to the boardwalk. I forgot all about pizza. Even the drifting scent of candy from the NutShack over to my left didn't lure me away. An hour passed. Maybe two. I watched and listened, unable to tear myself from the performance of this outrageous clown.

[36]For the first time in my life, I knew something for dead certain. Some way, somehow, I had to have a turn. Not throwing balls at the target. I wasn't going to waste money trying to dunk the Bozo. No, I wanted to be on the other side. I wanted to make the marks dance like puppets on a string. I wanted to shout and scream at the world from the safety of a cage.

[37]I wanted to be the Bozo.

Connect to the Author

David Lubar believes humor is an important part of learning. "The world is far too serious a place, especially for kids," Lubar says. "Some people act as if laughter doesn't belong in education. That's dead wrong. Kids need to explore, experiment, create, and have fun." Lubar, who was born in 1954 in Morristown, New Jersey, also likes to inject a little danger into his books. This element of danger is what drew him to the carnival as a setting for his novel *Dunk.* "Beneath the tackiness lurks that sense of danger," Lubar says. "It's not our world. We're just allowed to visit there."

Television
Commercial Script:

"Arthur Goes for It"

This is Arthur Beetleman. He needs help.

[1]Ad opens with an extreme long shot of a teenage male standing on the sidewalk in front of his school. Hip-hop music can be heard faintly in the background. The music continues throughout the ad.

ANNOUNCER: Meet Arthur Beetleman.

[2]Audience hears an audible camera click. Camera then **focuses** on the face of a 14-year-old Caucasian male. His brown hair is unfashionably messy. He is wearing geeky glasses with thick, black frames. A strip of white tape holds one of the earpieces to the main frame of the glasses. Part of the clothing on his upper body can be seen. He's wearing a nerdy, short-sleeved button-front shirt. Over this, he is wearing a plaid sweater vest. The shirt collar is twisted up on one side. He has a generally clueless expression. Students pass by in the background. No one acknowledges the boy's presence.

ARTHUR: Uh, hi.

[3]Arthur gives an uncomfortable smile. He waves his hand in an awkward greeting.

ANNOUNCER: Obviously, Arthur needs some help. He wishes he had more friends. People treat him as if he were subhuman. He's not happy.

[4]Camera highlights a group of boys and girls talking and laughing, although what they're saying isn't clear. They are all comfortable in their skins. They clearly enjoy one another's company.

ANNOUNCER: He wishes that he were better looking.

[5]Camera picks out an attractive teenage African American male among the students milling around the front of the school. The boy turns toward the camera. He flashes a sparkling smile at the camera.

ANNOUNCER: He wishes that he were good at sports.

[6]Several very fit teen male runners jog past, in front of Arthur. They are all wearing matching school track shorts and jerseys.

ANNOUNCER: He wishes he knew how to dress like the cool kids.

[7]Camera highlights two teenage males. Both are dressed in cool-looking baggy jeans, shirts, and very stylish and expensive-looking athletic shoes. The camera lingers on the shoes.

ANNOUNCER: Yeah, you noticed the shoes. They're made by GO Shoes. They're the **standard** in cool footwear. Anything else is just . . . **primitive**.

[8]Camera pans down past Arthur's Bermuda shorts to show Arthur's feet tastelessly covered in brown socks and clunky dark leather sandals.

ANNOUNCER *in a scolding tone of voice*: REALLY, Arthur! At least you could've worn white socks.

[9]Camera moves back up to Arthur's face. He has a pitiful, apologetic expression. A male basketball celebrity such as LeBron James walks onscreen. He takes one look at Arthur with a surprised expression. He shakes his head to the camera. Then he turns to Arthur.

LEBRON *to Arthur*: Whoa! You need some help, bro'. You've gotta *look* cool if you wanna *be* cool. Let's start with some new shoes, man. Some GO shoes.

[10]Camera pans down to LeBron's shoes. They are the same expensive shoes as those worn by the boys shown earlier in the commercial.

ANNOUNCER: That's right. To be cool, you want to start from the ground up—with a pair of GO athletic shoes—the most finely tuned athletic shoes on the planet.

[11]Camera shows a handsome teenage Asian male. He is walking confidently down a sidewalk in a pair of GO athletic shoes.

ANNOUNCER: GO shoes not only *look* good, they're designed to do your feet good, too.

[12]Camera shows a closeup of a GO shoe, which rotates slowly and highlights specific parts of the shoe as the announcer describes them.

ANNOUNCER: The mesh upper part of the shoe allows your foot to breathe. The inner cushion comforts and protects your foot. The thick soles increase muscle activity in the heel region. It's like getting a workout without really trying. The unique inner sole construction improves your overall balance. You stand taller. You look more confident. The soles are made of durable space-age rubber. The waffle pattern protects you against slipping on slick surfaces. It's all you could ever want in an athletic shoe.

[13]Camera returns to the Asian boy, who is still strolling confidently down the sidewalk, smiling.

ANNOUNCER: Some guys claim that wearing GO footwear every day even helps strengthen their core muscles. What does that mean? It means abs of steel! You can develop the kind of body that other guys will envy and all the girls will notice.

[14]Camera shows a shot of a male torso, with well-developed abdominal muscles. Then it returns to Arthur, who looks slightly less distressed and more hopeful.

ANNOUNCER: So what do you say, Arthur. Want to GO for it?
ARTHUR: Yeah! I want people to notice me.
ANNOUNCER: What you mean is, you want them to notice you for the right reasons!

[15]Scene switches to Arthur sitting on a stool in a shoe store. He is trying on a pair of GO shoes. Next shot is of a cool-looking, handsome version of Arthur—hair in place, no glasses, fashionable T-shirt and jeans, and GO shoes. The teen is smiling confidently at the camera.

ANNOUNCER: So, Arthur—what do you think? Do the shoes make a difference?

[16]Camera pans over to the actual Arthur, who essentially looks the same as before, but with the cool shoes.

ARTHUR: Wow! I feel like a new person! My brother, Kip [Arthur points to the handsome teen next to him], says that I'm looking pretty good these days.
ANNOUNCER: GO shoes. At department stores and discount outlets . . . all over the planet.

[17]Black screen with white GO logo. The words "GO for it" flash onto the screen just before the fadeout.   [time: 1:00 minute]

White Guys Can't Rap

Who's rap is more correct, Kanye West (left) or the Beastie Boys (right)?

[1]Let's face the facts. White guys can't rap. Well, technically, they *can* rap. It's just that their rap is totally lame. Think about it. Vanilla Ice? Lame. Kid Rock? He's not even a real rapper. OK, there's Eminem. That dude's not bad. But everything Eminem knows he learned from Dr. Dre, and Dr. Dre is about as black as black gets. Hey, I'm just being honest here. Just think about your own personal rap heroes. How many of them are white?

289

²The simple fact is black people invented rap and came up with all the innovations that made rap what it is today. It all started in the 1970s, when a black Jamaican guy named Kool Herc brought "toasting" to New York City. Toasting, which was huge in Jamaica, involved chanting and improvising rhymes over the instrumental parts of reggae records. Kool Herc was the first to chant those immortal lines, "Throw your hands in the air. Wave 'em like you just don't care." What Kool Herc did wasn't called rap for many years, but it was the beginning of a new musical form.

³Kool Herc's toasting caught on in New York's black neighborhoods. Before long, it seemed like everyone was rapping over instrumental records. Then rap broke big in 1979, when the Sugar Hill Gang released "Rapper's Delight." It sold millions of copies and inspired many of today's biggest rap acts to pick up the microphone. Toasting had changed and would forever more be known as rap. And rap became big business.

⁴As rap developed over the years, all the best rappers were black. The list is long: Run DMC, LL Cool J, KRS-1, Eric B and Rakim, Public Enemy, Ice Cube, Tupac, Missy Elliott, Snoop Dogg, the Wu Tang Clan. These were the innovators in rap. They took rap to new heights and helped it grow into the world's most popular music. And they were all black. This was not a coincidence. Rap grew out of the black urban experience. Rappers were rapping about being poor and being discriminated against just because they were black. White rappers could imitate the style, but they couldn't really *feel* what they were rapping about. What do white people know about being discriminated against just because of the color of their skin?

⁵Sure, there have been some white rappers over the years. Most have been lame, like Vanilla Ice. Some have been pretty cool, like the Beastie Boys and Eminem. There also have been some great Latino rap acts like Cypress Hill and Fat Joe. Some of these rappers have made serious contributions to rap music. But at the end of the day, they're all imitators, not innovators. They just can't relate to the urban black experience any more than you or I could relate to the experience of being a Martian. And since white rappers can't relate to the black experience, you can't expect black people to relate to what they are rapping about. If you need more proof, just look at all the winners of Grammy Awards for rap. Put all the rap Grammy winners on a stage, and you're not going to see many white faces. There's a reason for that.

Rap Belongs to Everyone Now

[6]**M**y name is Caesar Alexander. If you haven't heard of me already, you will soon. Someday I'm going to conquer the world, just like the ancient Roman emperor Caesar and the ancient ruler Alexander the Great. Only instead of using armies, this Caesar Alexander will be conquering the world with "two turntables and a microphone," and the best rap on the planet. Count on it.

[7]Now, I know a lot of people think that white guys like me can't rap. That's only because they haven't heard me yet. It's true that there have been plenty of lame white rappers over the years. But there has been no shortage of lame black rappers, either. (MC Hammer, I'm looking at you.) My point is, it doesn't matter what color your skin is; your rap is either legit or it isn't.

[8]No doubt, you have to give proper respect to the contributions of black rappers. Urban blacks invented rap and turned it into a monster force in the music world. But white rappers played an important role, too. For example, did you know that the first number 1 rap song was recorded by a white band? Look it up. In 1980, the band Blondie used elements of rap in their number 1 single "Rapture."

[9]That brings up one of the most important contributions to rap music white rappers have made. White musicians have led the way in

Caesar Alexander is planning to conquer the world—with music.

blending rap with other forms of music. Blondie blended rap with punk and new wave music to make "Rapture." Guys like Beck blended rap with folk and rock music. Bands like Linkin Park mixed rap and heavy metal music. Those innovations have played an important role in helping rap conquer the world.

[10]A lot of folks point to the Grammy Awards as evidence that black rappers are the best. But what does that really prove? The Grammy Awards are like popularity contests. You win because people like you, not because you're the best. Most of the greatest music ever made was never even nominated for a Grammy. Ask 10 people to name the greatest guitar player who ever lived. Nine of them—or maybe all 10—will say Jimi Hendrix. Guess how many Grammy Awards Hendrix won during his all-too-brief life. Zero. That's how meaningful Grammy Awards are.

[11]Some people say white people can't truly understand rap because they don't know what it's like to be poor and discriminated against. That's crazy, and I'm living proof. I grew up in the same poor New York neighborhood where rap first took root. When I was growing up, we never knew where our next meal would come from. Sometimes it didn't come at all. We lived in a rat-infested apartment building with peeling wallpaper and carpets crusted in filth. The hallways smelled like something crawled underneath the stairs and died. People were screaming, yelling, and arguing all night. The place sounded like an insane asylum. I wore clothes that had been handed down two or three times. They never fit right, and there always seemed to be holes in the elbows of my shirts and the knees of my pants. So don't tell me I don't know what it's like to be poor.

[12]And, as a white rapper, I definitely know what it's like to be discriminated against. People see the color of my skin and automatically say, "That white boy can't rap." But I don't get mad. I just grab the mic and prove them all wrong. By the time I get to rocking the party, everyone's too busy dancing and acting crazy to worry about the color of my skin. And that's the way it should be.

[13]Rap doesn't belong to just one group of people. It belongs to the whole world. There are rap acts from black countries like Senegal, white countries like England, eastern European countries like Bulgaria, and Asian countries like Mongolia. Almost every kind of music has been blended with rap, even classical music. Like Caesar and Alexander, rap music has conquered the world. Now, it's time for Caesar Alexander to conquer the rap world.